ELIZABETH GEORGE

A Woman After God's Own Heart®

A Bible Study Workbook

SAMPSON
RESOURCES

CONTENTS

Introduction

A Heart for God's Word

Introduction

A Heart for God's Word

Dear beloved sister, what an honor and privilege to walk hand in hand with you down the path of our dreams—that of becoming women after God's own heart! This is truly a noble and righteous goal, isn't it? And God wants to come alongside us to strengthen and empower us as we take this walk—a walk toward becoming His kind of women.

God will indeed do His work. But there is something you and I must do as well. In Acts 13:22 we find this lofty goal for our lives. Here we read God's description of His servant David: *"I have found David the son of Jesse, a man after My own heart, who will do all My will"* (NKJV). Did you catch it? God's desire for us as women after His heart is that we do all *His* will. I pray that as we walk through this workbook and as you watch the video, we will both covenant with the Lord to look for His will throughout this study...and then, with God's grace and help, *do* His will.

I know your schedule is tight. I know you are a busy woman. The daily lessons are written so you can get the most benefit from a short, concentrated period of study. If you will devote about thirty minutes every day, five days a week, you can gain the biblical insight and truth you need for your busy week. Set aside this brief period of time and protect it as your personal appointment with the Lord. I promise that you will receive a great blessing from your time in God's Word.

As you pray and prepare for your group meetings, plan to share with the women there what God is teaching you. Go with the idea of being the "older" or mature woman that Titus 2:3 describes. Go with a heart for giving, for encouraging, for participating. Go to bless that one who is hurting. Go to be blessed, but also go to be a blessing to others. My prayer is that you will continue to strive to be a woman after God's own heart, a beautiful woman who will do all His will! This, dear one, is indeed "precious in the sight of God" (1 Peter 3:4, NKJV).

Hearing God's Heart

Luke 10:38–42; 2 Timothy 3:16–17

Key Truths:

❖ Those who hope in the Lord will renew their strength.

❖ Those who abide in Christ will bear much fruit.

❖ We can do everything through Christ, who gives us strength.

> *Learning that in Him we live and move and have our being, we are slowly conformed to His image. Thus and only thus, in what the old Puritans called "creaturely" dependence and obedience, we become fully human and fully free.*
>
> **— Elisabeth Elliot —**

Video Notes

Wait upon the lord.
Without God we can do nothing

1. Give time to the lord.
2. First things first – God first
3. First time let it be early in the morning
   prepare to meet the day.

—

1. Refuse to miss the day
2. Be a women of one Book (the book)
3. Beat the family up.
4. purpose to get up
5. Open the book of God.

Week One

A Heart for Blessing in Prayer

"God desires for us to have a heart for prayer."

A Heart for Blessing in Prayer

"God desires for us to have a heart for prayer."

Psalm 5:3; 88:13; Matthew 6:5-15; Hebrews 11:6

Key Truths:

❖ Jesus devoted the early morning to prayer.

❖ God rewards those who earnestly and wholeheartedly seek Him.

❖ Our relationship with God and with others influences the effectiveness of our prayers.

This week's verse to remember:

"Pray without ceasing."

1 Thessalonians 5:17 (NKJV)

How can you and I become women devoted to God, women who live for God and love Him deeply? The answer—and the journey toward becoming women after God's own heart—begins with prayer! When we commune with God in prayer and experience that deeper relationship with Him, we grow spiritually in a multitude of ways, ways we'll be addressing throughout this workbook.

But for now, as we approach this first week of lessons, let's take first things first! We both want our relationship with God to reign in our hearts. I know that, like me, you want to walk so closely with Him that His fragrance permeates all of your life and refreshes all who cross your path. This happens when you and I meet with God in prayer, on bended knee, prostrate in soul and humble in heart.

As we look more closely at the spiritual discipline of prayer and its blessings in our lives, we must realize that prayer is one way God has provided for us to commune with Him, and when you and I accept His invitation to commune with Him, He will transform our hearts and change our lives.

Day One: The Journey Begins!

Hearing from God

1. Think about your typical day—your usual routine of waking up, preparing for the day, and fulfilling your responsibilities. What things make it difficult for you to spend time in prayer?

In a hurry to get started on my routine for the day.

2. God's Word challenges and inspires us to make prayer a part of everyday life. Read the following scriptures, and write down what you learn about prayer.

Psalm 5:3; 88:13 *In the morning is when you hear my Voice & lay down my Request before you.*

Matthew 6:5-15 *Say the lords prayer*

Mark 1:35-38 *Jesus went away by himself to pray early in the morning*

James 5:16 *Confess your sins to ea other & pray for each other. The prayer of a rightous man is powerful & effective*

3. God provides great encouragement and instruction for us whenever we desire to seek Him. His Word sets a clear path for us to follow. Read the following scriptures, and identify the hope and instruction that God provides us when we seek to know Him.

Deuteronomy 4:29 *If you look for God with all your heart and soul you will find him*

1 Chronicles 28:9 *If you seak him he will be found by you.*

2 Chronicles 16:9 *God looks for those who are committed to him and strengthens them*

Psalm 119:2 *Blessed are those who seak him with all their heart.*

Hebrews 11:6 *Without faith it is impossiable to please him*

Responding to God: "Yes, but how?"

4. Getting started is often the hardest part of any challenge. God's Word provides inspiration to help us move beyond the starting line. Read the following scriptures, and jot down phrases that can help you start on your quest to develop a heart for prayer.

   Jeremiah 33:3 *Call to me & I will tell you great and Unsearchable things you do not know*

   Matthew 7:7-8 *Knock & the door will be opened to you seek & you will find — to him who knocks the door will be opened*

   James 4:3 *When you ask you do not receive because you ask with wrong motives, That you spend what you get on your pleasures*

   1 Peter 5:8-9 *The devil roams around like a roaring lion He will devour everything — Resist him*

5. Here are three simple steps you can take to begin your journey toward a daily devotional time with God. Commit to do these three simple things this week. When you have completed a task, check the box to the left.

   ❑ Obtain a notebook or booklet that will become your daily prayer journal. Use this journal to list your prayer concerns and the many ways the Lord answers your prayers.

   ❑ Dedicate a specific time of day for your time with the Lord. Consider it an appointment that you must keep.

   ❑ Dedicate a specific place for your devotional time. Choose a place that minimizes interruptions and distractions.

> *May I be careful to maintain a constant, habitual sense of Thee in my mind; to live and act as in Thy presence; to think often of Thee. May I ever remember that I am in the presence of the great and holy God.*
>
> — **Susanna Wesley** —

LifeScene

Linda has been a Christian for twenty years. She actively serves the Lord in her church and works hard to be a good parent to her three children, ages three, five, and nine. Her husband, Dave, seldom goes to church and resents the time she is away with the kids at church. Linda has tried several times to establish a daily devotional habit but with limited success. Her part-time job and her roles as mother, wife, and Sunday School teacher demand more time than she has to give. She often wakes up more tired than when she went to bed. Linda lives with a nagging sense of guilt about not spending time in prayer.

If Linda came to you and expressed her frustration about finding a daily time for prayer, how would you respond? Jot down your thoughts in the space below.

Maybe in her Car or in bed at night. or just demand a quiet time !!

Summary

For many believers, early morning is ideal for spending time with God in prayer and Bible study. God's Word tells us that anyone who earnestly seeks God will find Him and hear from Him. May the Lord bless you as you begin this journey.

Today, Lord, the prayer of my heart is Peace & Comfort for Warren, Safe traveling for all the family my 2 sons to become one with you. Bible to draw close Me to learn more and Know how to act upon it.

Day Two: The Blessing of Greater Faith

Matthew 7:7-8; John 15:7-8; 1 John 5:14-15

Hearing from God

1. An essential aspect of prayer is faith. When we pray, we must have faith that God hears us and will answer our prayers. Read the two scriptures below, and write down the images David used to describe God.

   Psalm 61:2 from the ends of the earth I call to you he calls to God everywhere he is - until he is weak lead me to Jesus

   Psalm 62:6 God is his rock and strength and I will Not be shaken ~

2. An American car company advertises its trucks with the phrase "like a rock." How has God been a rock in your life?

   He brought me out of a terriable life that I had No hope of giting out - He has placed me in a safe place.

3. Hannah was a desperate woman who cried out to God. Read about her in 1 Samuel 1. Then respond to the questions below.

   A. What indications do you see that Hannah sought God with all her heart?

   She prayed every day and Cried out to him.

   B. How did God respond to Hannah's prayer? He gave her a Son.

   C. How did Hannah respond to God's gracious yes? She dedicated Samuel to God

John Wesley spent at least two hours each day in prayer.

〜

Samuel Rutherford rose at 3 AM daily to wait upon God.

〜

Alexander MacLaren owed his success "to the habit, never broken, of spending one hour a day" alone with the Eternal.

〜

Martin Luther said, "I have so much to do today that I shall spend the first three hours in prayer."

4. Our faith in God grows as we pray and experience His answers to our prayers. David wrote about the attention God gives to the righteous who cry out to Him. Read Psalm 34:15–18, and summarize in your words how God helps those who cry out to Him.

He hears those who cry out to him He delivers them from all their troubles

5. The New Testament teaches us how God hears the prayers of those who love Christ and abide in Him. Jot down the truths you find in these scriptures.

Matthew 7:7-8 *He answers all those who seek him*

John 15:7-8 *If we remain his he grants whatever we ask*

1 John 5:14-15 *Jesus said stop sining or something bad may happen.*

6. Sometimes we sabotage our prayers by praying for the wrong reasons. Read James 4:1–3, and identify this problem in our prayers.

We ask for things with the wrong reason for wanting it. We want it for our own pleasures.

Responding to God: "Yes, but how?"

7. What obstacles are keeping you from establishing and maintaining a regular time of prayer and communion with the Lord?

Just have not set a pattern

8. Praying with faith is easier said than done. If you were asked to explain in simple words what "praying with faith" means, how would you reply?

praying knowing God is hearing you Knowing he will answer even if it No. Knowing his time may not be ours.

9. Do you know someone whose faith needs encouragement? What can you do this week to encourage that person to pray with faith?

Talk with them about it. read the bible to them

LifeScene *Donna discovered that her good friend Nicole was diagnosed with a rare form of leukemia. Donna decided to pray and fast. She prayed earnestly that God would heal Nicole. A few months later Nicole died, leaving behind her husband and three children. Donna's faith in God's goodness and in prayer was deeply scarred. Now she seldom prays, and she lives with a sense of betrayal and bitterness.*

How do you think you would have responded if you had been Donna? What scriptures would you choose to share with her?

I would have been sad but not angry with God.

Summary

An essential aspect of prayer is faith. Our faith in God grows as we pray and experience God's answers to our prayers. Doubts and life struggles can discourage us, but we can know that God hears and responds to the prayers of those who abide in Him. We can experience the blessing of greater faith as we pray.

Heavenly Father, the prayer of my heart today is Peace & Comfort for my brother - a closer walk with God. To be able to draw very near.

Day Three: The Blessing of Greater Peace

John 14:26–27; Galatians 5:22–26; Philippians 4:6–9

Hearing from God

1. Greater peace comes to women who pray faithfully. Take a moment to read Philippians 4:6–9; then in the space below write what you learn about prayer and peace.

What ever is good and praises to God will be with you

2. John 14:26-27 contains Jesus' words regarding the ministry of the Holy Spirit, who intercedes in our prayers. In the same passage, Jesus talks about the peace He came to bring to you. Read these verses, and meditate on the times the Lord has brought peace into your life. How is the peace of Jesus Christ different from any other?

_____

_____

_____

_____

3. Galatians 5:22-26 lists the fruit of the Spirit that comes to those who "live by" or "keep in step with" the Holy Spirit. Prayer is a primary way of staying in step with God's Spirit. List the attributes of personality (fruit of the Spirit) that come to women who through prayer and submission to God stay in step with the Holy Spirit.

Love, Joy, peace, patience, Kindness goodness, gentleness and self controle

_____

4. Paul wrote to believers in Colossae that they should allow the peace of God to rule in their hearts (Col. 3:15). How can spending time in prayer determine who or what controls your day?

God determines our day and prayer will help us be the way that God wants us to be

_____

5. To his friends in Thessalonica, Paul wrote, "Now may the Lord of peace himself give you peace at all times and in every way" (2 Thess. 3:16). Think about the day ahead of you. Note the parts of your day when you especially need God's peace. Jot down those moments in the space below. Then pause and ask the Lord to grant you peace during those times.

There is no one part of my day that I need God more since I need him at all times

_____

6. Sometimes when we are going through hardship or suffering, we are actually experiencing the loving discipline of our Heavenly Father. Our first impulse is to pray for deliverance from our hardship or trial, but God may be using the trial to lead us into a greater peace. Read Hebrews 12:7-11. Based on this scripture, how should we pray in times of trouble? Write down your thoughts.

That we take the ~~discipline~~ discipline well, learn from it and ask God to help us through

_____

Responding to God: "Yes, but how?"

7. What life concerns are robbing you of peace at this moment?

_____

_____

_____

_____

Stop and pray. Ask the Lord to fill you with His peace as you entrust each concern to His control.

8. Fear, stress, anxiety, and depression are disabling emotions that keep many women on the sidelines of church involvement. You may have a fear of failing. You may fear being unable to meet God's lofty expectations. You may fear commitment. If you are not currently serving in your church, what is needed in your life to free you to serve the Lord?

I try to serve in Church, but I am very shy and feel inadequate

_____

9. Perhaps you are currently serving, but you find God's peace elusive because you are carrying too heavy a load of responsibilities elsewhere. Pause and pray. Ask the Lord to reveal how you should manage your responsibilities without sacrificing the peace you find through prayer. Jot down any thoughts that come to you while you are praying.

My Concentration

_____

_____

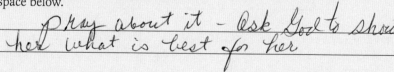

LifeScene

Gwen lives a fast-paced life as an attorney. She manages several cases, many of which will change people's lives for years. The stress is intense, and the days are long. Gwen recently became a Christian and started reading the Bible. She read the scriptures about prayer and the peace of God mentioned in this lesson but is genuinely skeptical that she can find peace in her demanding occupation. She asks her pastor whether she should give up practicing law and pursue another career that would allow her more time for prayer and spiritual growth.

What do you think Gwen should do? Write down your thoughts in the space below.

Pray about it - Ask God to show her what is best for her

_____

_____

Summary

Greater peace comes to women who pray faithfully. By keeping in step with God through prayer, we allow the Holy Spirit to bring peace into our lives. By focusing on Christ daily through prayer, we can experience God's peace regardless of the hectic day before us. We are not without hope. Christ is our hope and peace in every day.

Today, dear Lord, the prayer of my heart is To draw me closer

Day Four: The Blessing of Greater Purity

Psalm 51; 1 John 1:8-9

Hearing from God

1. God's Word frequently urges us to confess our sins and to seek God's forgiveness. Read the following scriptures that focus on confession: Psalm 32:5; Proverbs 28:13; James 5:16; 1 John 1:8-9. Select the scripture that means the most to you, and copy it verbatim in the space below.

   He who conceals his sins does not prosper but whoever confesses and renounces them finds mercy.

2. Because God expects us to live lives of purity and holiness, prayer is essential to confessing our sin and restoring purity. Read these scriptures, and jot down other biblical teachings on how to nurture purity in your life.

   Psalm 24:3-4 _____

   _____

   Psalm 119:9 _____

   _____

   Philippians 1:9-11 _____

   _____

   Philippians 2:14-16 _____

   _____

   Philippians 4:8 _____

   _____

3. When confronted with his sin by the prophet Nathan, David repented in earnest and wrote a psalm of confession. Read Psalm 51, and then list some requests David made of God as he confessed his sin.

Blot out my transgressions, wash away my iniquity, cleanse me from my sins, teach me wisdom, Create me a pure heart

4. List at least three things David said he would do in response to God's forgiveness and cleansing.

1. *Cleanse Me & I will be clean*
2. *Wash me &, I will be whiter than snow*
3. *I will teach transgressors your way*

5. Read Matthew 7:3–5. Why do we find it easy to detect sin in someone else's life but remain blind to our own sin?

It is easier to see someone elses faults than our own.

Responding to God: "Yes, but how?"

6. Take a moment to read Psalm 139:23–24. Ask the Lord to search your heart for the next few minutes. Then ask Him to bring to mind any sin that He sees in your life. As God brings to mind your sinful thoughts, words, or actions, write them down in the space below. Then pray, specifically naming each sin and asking God to forgive you and to cleanse you.

7. After praying and confessing your sins, look at your list in question 6. Read Ephesians 4:1–3. Ask the Lord to remind you of people you need to confess to and seek their forgiveness. List any names that come to mind, and make appointments today to call or visit these persons. Your willingness to admit your errors and seek forgiveness may help repair broken relationships and restore Christian unity.

8. If you have carried out all or most of the assignments listed above, describe the inner sense of cleansing and purity that the Lord has given you.

I have ask for forgiveness from God I also ask to help me to not do them again

As women who are called to righteousness, godliness, faith, love...and prayer, we must not deny our sin, nor blame others for it, nor hide it, nor rationalize it. No, we must confess it, for it is the effective, fervent prayer of a righteous woman that avails much!

— **Elizabeth George** —

LifeScene *Denise knows that she overreacted and said hurtful things to her husband, Ken. In the heat of the moment, Ken responded in the same manner. He brought up issues in Denise's life that embarrassed her and made her feel small. Ken frequently belittles Denise's church involvement and seems to relish opportunities to expose what he calls her hypocrisy. Denise and Ken have hardly spoken to each other since their argument. Denise finds it impossible to pray or study her Bible, making her feel even worse about herself.*

What would you suggest Denise do in this situation?

Tell Ken she is sorry ask Ken to not speak of her church involvements. Ask God to keep her from being a hypocrisy.

Summary

We miss the blessing of greater purity when we fail to confess our sins and seek God's forgiveness. Ask the Lord to reveal your sins to you, and then take immediate action to confess and repent. Quickly go to those you have wronged, and make things right. Regain the blessing of greater purity.

Today, Lord, the prayer of my heart is _____

_____

_____

_____

Day Five: Praying Continually

1 Thessalonians 5:17

Hearing from God

1. One of the shortest verses in the Bible is 1 Thessalonians 5:17, but these words are profoundly important for a woman after God's own heart. Take a moment to read this verse in its context by reading all of 1 Thessalonians 5. After reading the chapter, ponder these questions: How can a person actually pray continually? What do you think is the underlying message here?

Keep prayers on your heart through the day

2. The command to pray continually sounds simple at first, but it involves a lifetime of application and devotion. The following passages remind us how we can make prayer an integral part of our lives. Some of these verses are repeated from previous lessons this week. Read them again, and jot down a reminder of the truth you draw from each scripture.

Psalm 5:3 *Pray in the morning ask for help throughout the day.*

Psalm 55:17 *I ask for help repeatly and he hears me.*

Psalm 119:164 *Praise him for his blessings*

Mark 1:35 *Go to a quiet place to pray*

3. How can praying daily in the early morning hours tune your heart for praying without ceasing the rest of the day?

You start your day with pray and continue on through the day —

4. Paul prayed continually for his friends in Thessalonica. Read 2 Thessalonians 1. What did Paul believe would result from his constant prayers for his friends?

Their faith is growing. There love for one another was growing

5. God wants to accomplish every good purpose in your life. Praying continually is a key to realizing and achieving God's purpose in your life. At this point in your life with Christ, what do you believe God's purpose is for you?

To make me a worthy person worthy to live in heaven with him.

Responding to God: "Yes, but how?"

6. Continual prayer is not meaningless repetition, nor is it praying without a break. Praying continually means praying in any circumstance. At any time during the day, you can breathe a prayer to the Lord, talk aloud to Him as you drive, or continue to express your thanks to God in a hymn or song of praise. In the left column below, list some issues that are heavy on your heart. In the right column, list some blessings you have received from God.

My deepest concerns	My blessings and praises
My Children	*They are learning*
My worthiness	*I am learning*

> *Prayer is spiritual breathing. You take a breath in...and a prayer goes out!*
>
> — **Elizabeth George** —

7. Chances are that you don't need to look at this list to remember these concerns and blessings. Throughout your day today, breathe a prayer to the Lord about these concerns. Give them to Him. Release them. Then thank Him and praise Him for blessings in your life.

8. As we have studied, the early morning is an ideal time to "beat your family up" and have your time alone with God. How successful have you been at establishing this time in your daily schedule?

   ❏ It hasn't worked for me.
   ❏ I've tried but...
   ❏ I like it!
   ❏ I think a different time of day would be better for me.
   ❏ I prefer *I have not started as yet*

9. Whatever results you have experienced, do not be discouraged. Establishing a new habit takes time. Everyone has ups and downs, breakthroughs and setbacks. Set your heart on the goal, give yourself fully to the Lord, and He will help you find and keep your daily time with Him.

> *But I will sing of your strength,*
> *in the morning I will sing of your love;*
> *for you are my fortress,*
> *my refuge in times of trouble.*
>
> *O my Strength, I sing praise to you;*
> *you, O God, are my fortress, my loving God. (Ps. 59:16-17)*

LifeScene *Rylie works third shift at a local hospital. As a single parent, she lives with her parents, who help care for her daughter, Bryn. An unhappy and abusive marriage left Rylie with deep emotional scars and smoldering anger at God. Every evening she wrestles with God. Sometimes patients ask her to pray for them, and she even hears patients pray for her at times. Rylie wants to be able to pray freely again, but she doesn't know where to start. Her life seems so hectic and confused.*

In the space that follows, write Rylie a short note, encouraging her toward a closer walk with the Lord through prayer.

Dear Rylie, *Just start praying and believing*

Summary *Believe all things*

God's Word challenges us to pray without ceasing, to pray continually. This means to pray in any circumstance of life throughout the day. A day of prayer requires a heart for God and a belief that He hears you when you pray. Beginning your day with time alone with God helps set a pattern in which prayer can be your theme and focus.

Today, Lord, I want the continual prayer of my heart to be _____

Worthy of you

Video Notes

1. God is a rock
2. Our daughters be like Cornor stones
   Greater peace
   Cast all cares on him

3. greater purity –
   Confess our sins
   Is it true, Is it Kind, Is it helpful

Week Two

A Heart for Passion in Prayer

"A passionate prayer life transforms everything."

Week Two

A Heart for Passion in Prayer

"A passionate prayer life transforms everything."

Ephesians 6:18-20; Philippians 4:4-7; Hebrews 13:5-6

Key Truths:

❖ We can have great confidence in our decisions when prayer is part of every day.

❖ Trusting in God's sufficiency is central to greater contentment in life.

❖ Praying for others is a dynamic, powerful ministry that helps release the power of Almighty God.

We all have our passions, but the greatest passion we can desire and nurture is a passion for God and for communing with Him through prayer. As we step into another exciting lesson regarding your prayer life, we are going to focus on several life-fulfilling blessings that come from a heart for passion in prayer.

God's Word includes numerous examples of people whose lives were transformed by trusting and seeking God. This week we will discover how a passion for prayer can give us greater confidence in decision making. Too often we make decisions based on selfish and limited perspectives. God has a longer-range view and gives us greater wisdom whenever we seek His will and way.

One of the most debilitating emotions in the lives of women today is discontentment. We will look at how a passion for prayer reshapes the way we view the world and what we value. Several women in Scripture modeled contentment and provide great examples for women today who get distracted by pale competitors to God's best.

A passion for prayer enables a woman after God's own heart to find her unique and powerful ministry within the kingdom of God. Throughout the centuries since the life of Jesus Christ, women who pray have gained the blessings of greater dependence on God, a humble heart, a joyful spirit, and richer relationships with others. May these blessings and more be yours as you seek a heart for passion in prayer.

This week's verse to remember:

"Praying always with all prayer and supplication in the Spirit, being watchful to this end with all perseverance and supplication for all the saints."

Ephesians 6:18 (NKJV)

Day One: The Blessing of Greater Confidence in Decision Making

Jeremiah 17:9; Luke 22:39-46

Hearing from God

1. As we begin a new week pursuing a heart for God, review the lessons from last week. In the space below, write the blessings of prayer we have already studied.

The blessing of *Greater Faith*

The blessing of *Greater Peace*

The blessing of *Greater Purity*

2. Several people mentioned in the Bible made poor decisions. Read these scriptures, and jot down a few words identifying these poor decisions.

Genesis 3:1-7 *Eve when she ate forbidden fruit*

Genesis 11:1-9 *The Tower of Babel - when God scattered the laungage*

Genesis 37:17b-35 *Joseph sold by his brothers their father mourned for his son*

Exodus 1:8-14 *Pharah - Made slaves of the Isralites*

Numbers 13:17-14:4 _____

3. Other biblical characters sought to hear from God and then followed His leadership in their decisions. Read these scriptures, and identify the decisions that were made.

Genesis 12:1-4 *Abram - He did as the lord said & he was blessed*

Genesis 22:1-18 *Abraham - God tested him but he did as God said & he was blessed.*

Genesis 24:10-18 *Isaac - prayed for a sign for a wife and God sent Rebecca*

Judges 7:1-12 *Gideon - The lord seperated his men for him*

1 Kings 3:1-15 *Soloman - God came to him in a dream.*

4. Right before He was arrested, Jesus agonized while He prayed in the garden. Take a moment to read Luke 22:39-46. After reading this scripture, respond to the following questions.

Why do you think Jesus agonized in prayer? *He dreaded to be Crusified*

> *Out of the will of God there is no such thing as success; in the will of God there cannot be any failure.*
>
> **—Author Unknown—**

Do you think Jesus reached a decision through His prayer, or do you think He gained something else? Explain your response.

He gained strength through the Angels

Responding to God: "Yes, but how?"

5. Why do you think many of us do not take time to pray before we make decisions? What are our most common excuses?

We take amatters into our own hands because we think we can handle it.

6. Read Jeremiah 17:9. How has your heart or your desires led you astray in previous decisions? Jot down a brief, candid example.

Lots of times

7. Think for a moment about decisions you will have to make today or later this week. List some of these decisions below.

8. Pause for a moment and pray, asking the Lord to override your personal desires and wants. Ask Him to guide you and to reveal His will for you today regarding each of these decisions.

> *Forbid that I should venture on any business without first begging Thy direction and assistance.*
>
> — **Susanna Wesley** —

LifeScene

Carrie was positive that God had brought Carlton into her life. Having made a mistake with her first marriage, which ended in a painful divorce, Carrie knew that she would never repeat that mistake. Carlton was not like her husband. He was patient, kind to her children, and attentive to her needs. Carrie's friends did not share her optimism about Carlton and urged her to pray about her decision. They advised her to talk to others in Carlton's past, but Carrie rejected their advice and said, "The past is the past. People can change." She didn't feel she needed to pray anymore. She had been praying for three years for God to send her someone. Now God had brought her Carlton. So she continued making plans for her wedding.

What do you think about Carrie's decision? What actions, if any, should she take next? *She most definetely needs to take her friends advice and talk to people of his past & to pray.*

Summary

Godly people can make ungodly decisions if they don't seek God through prayer. The Bible includes many examples of people who made poor decisions because of selfishness, anger, or desire. Our heart is deceitful, so we must spend time with God in prayer and ask Him to reveal His will and way to us. We can have confidence in our decisions when we make prayer an important part of daily life.

Today, Lord, the prayer of my heart is _to Curb my desire for earthly things_

Day Two: The Blessing of Greater Contentment, Part 1

Philippians 4:10-13; Hebrews 13:5-6; James 4:1-10

Hearing from God

1. This week we are focusing on developing a heart for passion in prayer. Find a dictionary, look up the word "passion," and write down its definition.

   A powerful emotion or appetite such as love, Joy, hate or anger or greed

2. The apostle Paul experienced more setbacks and suffering than most believers today. Read in 2 Corinthians 11:21-33 about a few of his experiences. Write down some of the traumatic experiences in Paul's life.

   beaten, lost at sea, Hungry, Cold In danger from false brothers or Country men from Bandits

3. In spite of his sufferings and persecution, Paul was able to experience contentment. Read Philippians 4:10-13. What was Paul's secret for finding contentment in every situation and circumstance of life?

   "I can do everything through him Who gives me strength"

4. Read Hebrews 13:5–6. What does this scripture identify as a source of discontentment in life?

   Money , Immorality

5. What does this passage teach about the pathway to contentment? What truths about God are described in these scriptures?

   He will never leave you – What can man do to me with God on your side

6. God's Word provides additional truths about finding contentment in life. Read these scriptures, and summarize briefly the teaching about contentment.

   Psalm 34:9 *Fear the lord & you will lack nothing*

   Psalm 84:5 *Blessed are those who's strength is in you.*

   Matthew 6:31–33 *Do not worry about tomorrow God knows our needs & all these things will be given you*

   Hebrews 10:32–39 *Keep you confidence*

> *The way to worry about nothing is to pray about everything.*
>
> —*Author Unknown*—

7. James 4:1–10 is a key scripture for understanding why we struggle to be content today. Read this passage, and then fill in the two columns that follow. List the reasons we lack contentment, and then list the ways God's Word says we can avoid fights, quarreling, and unhappiness.

Reasons for Quarreling, Fighting, and Unrest	**God's Guidelines for Peace and Contentment**
desires	*Ask God what you desire and do not pray for pleasures.*
You want but do not ask God	*Be Humble*
Wrong motives	
friendship with the world	
do not be proud	

Responding to God: "Yes, but how?"

8. Based on what you have learned today by reading these scriptures, what is lacking in your life that robs you of joy and contentment?

   desire Human pleasures

9. Review your responses to questions 3, 5, and 6. What do you need to change about your life to achieve greater contentment and peace with God?

    learn to be Content. Learn to ask God for my needs and colecisions

10. Stop right now and pray. Confess every sin and issue that is drawing you away from being content. Ask the Lord to help you apply what you have learned today, and commit to seek His peace and contentment whenever you are anxious or restless.

LifeScene Rhonda grew up with an alcoholic father and a mother who worked two jobs. Now that she is an adult, she has her own family. Both Rhonda and her husband work because they have four children, a mortgage, and a large credit-card debt. Life is anything but peaceful in her home. Her children frequently disrespect her and seldom obey. Most of the time Rhonda hides her desperation well, but today she breaks down while talking to you. She asks why you seem to be at peace and content with your life. She asks, "How do you do it?"

What is your answer?

pray, Pray & pray Contentment will follow

Summary

Life is full of setbacks and trials, but God wants us to trust Him and find contentment in Him. By making Christ the Lord of our lives, by having a healthy fear of God, and by trusting in God's sufficiency and power, we can experience greater contentment. The love of money and selfish desires can rob us of the peace God intended for us to have. Spending time in prayer will help us align our lives with Christ and grant us the blessing of greater contentment.

Lord, today I want to experience the blessing of greater contentment in my life. My prayer is *Work With me and I will work with you*

Day Three: The Blessing of Greater Contentment, Part 2

Psalm 16:5–11; Isaiah 26:3–4; Luke 10:38–42

Hearing from God

1. Find your dictionary again, and look up the definition of "contentment." Write the definition in the space below.

   Contentment Satification

2. Like Paul, we need to learn to trust God and find contentment no matter what life brings our way. Read these Old Testament scriptures, and identify truths that can increase your level of contentment.

   Psalm 16:5–11 *I have been assigned as my portion you have made my lot secure*

   Psalm 37:4–11 *Delight yourself in the lord and he will give you desires of your heart.*

   Psalm 118:24 *This is the day the lord has made. Let us rejoice & be glad in it.*

   Isaiah 26:3–4 *Trust in the lord, The lord is the rock eternal*

3. Which of these scriptures most caught your attention? List the scripture reference, and explain why its words are meaningful to you.

   Psalm 16:5–11 – I have been assigned my portion you have made my lot secure.

4. Several women in the Bible modeled contentment; however, contentment eluded other women. Read about these women in the scriptures below, and in the space that follows write a truth you have gained from their lives.

   Rachel—Genesis 30:1–3 *She wanted a son so her husband would love her – finally she found contentment in God*

   Manoah's wife—Judges 13:1–5 *She believed in God and did as he ask.*

   The Shunammite woman—2 Kings 4:8–14 *She was kind to the man of God & she trusted him fully*

   Elizabeth—Luke 1:5–7 *She was old but given a son*

   Mary—Luke 10:38–42 *She was eager to her Jesus' word*

   Martha—Luke 10:38–41 *Was busy in prepration Jesus prefered Mary' attitude*

> To complain is an accusation against God. It questions God's wisdom and God's good judgment. God has always equated complaining with unbelief.... Why? Because to complain is to doubt God. It is the same thing as suggesting that God really doesn't know what He is doing.
>
> — **Don Baker** —

Responding to God: "Yes, but how?"

5. What have you learned about God—His nature, His power, His interactions with people in the Bible, and His love for you—that has helped you along the road to greater contentment?

   That he wants us to be happy
   That he forgives us.

6. We can know about God's nature, but until we truly believe and trust in God, we will continue to be discontent. What worries, thoughts, and current situations continue to erode your contentment?

   My Children's walk with God —
   why ineed to keep buying tho. I do
   not need.

7. Just as you did yesterday, stop now and pray. Confess every sin and issue that is drawing you away from contentment. Ask the Lord to help you trust in His nature and His Word. At every point of unrest or fear, seek His peace and contentment through continual prayer.

LifeScene Bonnie woke up in the emergency room in great pain. She remembered nothing about the accident the night before. Her doctor told her that she had suffered spinal cord damage and might never walk again. Her child Audrey was in intensive care, her life hanging in the balance. Although Bonnie's husband was out of town on business, her friends Carol, Jill, and Gina were at her bedside. The words they shared with Bonnie soothed her heart and brought hope and peace in her hour of desperation.

What do you think Carol, Jill, and Gina told Bonnie?

God is always with you.

Summary

When we set our hearts, minds, and plans on God, He gives us a secure foundation on which we can build lives marked by contentment and trust. When we delight in God—find our joy in obeying and serving Him—He will give us everything we need to be content. Only by orienting our lives to the ways of God can we understand what is truly important in life and, therefore, be content.

Today, Lord, I want to trust you more and experience your contentment. My prayer is _____

_____

_____

_____

Day Four: The Blessing of Greater Ministry through Prayer

James 5:16–18; Ephesians 6:18–20

Hearing from God

1. Look back over the lessons for the past eight days, and review the blessings we have discovered that come through prayer. List some of these blessings below.

   The blessing of _Greater faith_

   The blessing of _" peace_

   The blessing of _" purity_

   The blessing of _" Contentment_

   The blessing of _____

2. Women who have a heart for God and who pray faithfully will discover that their prayers are effective tools in accomplishing God's purposes. You have already read James 5:16, but read it again. Describe a situation in your life when you have seen the powerful effects of prayer.

   driveing in the snow

3. Continue reading verses 17 and 18 in James 5. How did the prayers of Elijah change the course of history? (Also see 1 Kings 18.)

   It did not rain for three years then he prayed for rain and it rained

4. Read Paul's prayer request of his friends in Ephesus (Ephesians 6:18–20). How did the Ephesians' prayers for Paul and their belief that God would answer their prayers enable Paul to serve God more effectively?

   Prayed in all occations, all kinds of prayers & requests.

5. Praying for others can be a powerful, effective ministry. Take a moment to read the following scriptures. List the people you should pray for.

   Matthew 5:44 _Love your enemies, Pray for them_

   Matthew 9:37–38 _____

   1 Timothy 2:1-2 _request Prayers and Thanksgiving for everyone_

   James 5:13–16 _If you are in trouble, Pray — If you are happy sing songs of Praise_

31

6. Abraham interceded (prayed for) the people in the city of Sodom. Read Genesis 18:20–33. From reading this scripture, what do you learn about God and intercessory prayer?

He is open to descussion. He wants to save us.

Responding to God: "Yes, but how?"

7. Review your responses to question 5. List the names of people you know who fit the descriptions in these scriptures.

Matthew 5:44 _____ *NO* _____

Matthew 9:37–38 *no* _____

1 Timothy 2:1–2 _____ *no* _____

James 5:13–16 _____ *uo.* _____

8. Stop and pray for these persons by name, remembering the truths you have learned from James 5.

9. If you do not know the leaders of your church's prayer ministry, call your church office. Write down the name and phone number of your church's prayer ministry leader(s) in the spaces below. Consider calling one of the leaders and volunteering to assist in that ministry. Commit to pray for the leader and the ministry.

Name: _____ Phone: _____

Name: _____ Phone: _____

> *The secret prayer chamber is a bloody battleground. Here violent and decisive battles are fought out. Here the fate of souls for time and eternity is determined, in quietude and solitude.*
>
> — **O. Hallesby** —

LifeScene

April is concerned about the education her children are receiving at their school. She hears negative reports from some parents and occasional stories from her children that cast doubt on the abilities of their teachers. Some of April's friends have taken their children out of the local school system and have turned to homeschooling. Other friends have enrolled their children in costly private schools. After worrying about this situation for several weeks, April believes that prayer will help her know what to do.

In what ways can prayer have a positive effect on this situation?

If she prays asking God what she should do then wait & see what happens to make her answer known to her.

Summary

Praying for others is a powerful, effective ministry. Prayer truly changes things and works in conjunction with God's amazing power to achieve supernatural results. God's Word gives us several guidelines for prayer, including what to pray and whom to pray for. As a woman after God's own heart, consider participating in your church's prayer ministry and experiencing the greater blessing of ministry through prayer.

Today, Lord, the prayer of my heart is _Learn How to pray better._

Day Five: More Blessings

1 Samuel 1:9–17; Ezra 10:1; Philippians 4:4–7

Hearing from God

1. So far we have counted six of God's blessings that come as we pray and develop a heart for passion in prayer. This lesson will examine even more blessings. Acknowledging our utter need for God's help is a blessing because in so doing we admit our **great dependence on God**. Read the following scriptures, and jot down the great needs of Isaac, Hannah, and David as they prayed to God for help.

    Genesis 25:21 _Isaac prayed for his wife because she was barren. The Lord answered_

    1 Samuel 1:9–17 _Hannah prayed and Eli also, and God answered_

    Psalm 5:1–3 _I pray to you each morning and lay my request before you._

2. Another blessing from prayer is the development of a **humble heart**. Read these scriptures, and identify the way each person or group of people expressed humility to the Lord.

    Exodus 4:31 _____

    Numbers 16:22 _____

    1 Kings 8:54 _____

    1 Kings 18:42 _____

> *And Satan trembles when he sees,*
> *The weakest saint upon his knees.*
>
> — **William Cowper** —

33

Ezra 10:1 _____

_____

Luke 18:13 _____

_____

3. Prayer also brings the blessing of a **joyful spirit**. How are prayer and praise related to a joyful spirit in these scriptures?

Philippians 4:4–7 _____

_____

1 Thessalonians 5:16–18 _____

_____

4. Faithful, passionate prayer can contribute to **improved relationships**. Read these scriptures, and note the relationships that Christ calls us to develop with others. As you read each scripture, list one way that prayer can improve this relationship.

Matthew 5:43–44 _____

_____

Romans 12:14, 20–21 _____

_____

1 Thessalonians 5:12–13 _____

_____

Titus 2:4 _____

_____

Responding to God: "Yes, but how?"

5. Identify which of these four additional blessings are needed most in your life by responding to the following self-assessment. Check the box that most closely identifies the value of each prayer blessing in your life.

Blessing	Needed	Important	Absolutely Essential
Great dependence on God	☐	☐	☐
A humble heart	☐	☐	☐
A joyful spirit	☐	☐	☐
Improved relationships	☐	☐	☐

6. For each blessing that you checked "absolutely essential," review the scripture passages in this lesson that relate to that blessing. In the space below, write down a simple plan that will move you closer to experiencing that blessing.

_____

_____

_____

_____

7. See how many of the blessings of prayer you can recall without checking your workbook. Write down the blessings you can remember. Check your responses by reviewing the lessons for the past two weeks.

The blessing of _____ *Peace* _____

The blessing of _____ *Purity* _____

The blessing of _____ *Contentment* _____

The blessing of _____ *Faith* _____

The blessing of _____ *Humble* _____

The blessing of _____

The blessing of _____

The blessing of _____

The blessing of _____

The blessing of _____

LifeScene

Blanche is one of the church's most capable Bible teachers. She has taught a women's Sunday School class for thirty-three years and has earned a reputation as a Bible scholar. Many in the church defer to her on spiritual issues and dare not debate biblical truth and theology with her. Blanche enjoys her influence in the church and frequently employs it in church business meetings. Blanche is not afraid of or intimidated by anyone in the church and truly believes she knows God's will on every issue.

Which blessing of prayer do you think Blanche is missing in her life? What do you think would help Blanche see her need for this blessing?

_____

_____

_____

_____

_____

Summary

Faithful prayer brings us more blessings in the form of a greater dependence on God, a humble heart, a joyful spirit, and improved relationships with God and others. Whenever we realize our deficiency in any of these blessings, we can go to God's Word and pray to our Heavenly Father. He will draw us closer to Him as we focus on our great need for Him in all areas of life.

Lord, I want to experience even more blessings through faithful prayer. Today the prayer of my heart is _____

_____

_____

_____

TEN WAYS TO IMPROVE YOUR PRAYER LIFE

1. Use a prayer list or notebook.

2. Schedule a prayer time each day.

3. Spend time praying with others.

4. Pray using Scripture.

5. Borrow from the prayers of others.

6. Open and close each day with a time of prayer.

7. Gain inspiration from the biographies of others who prayed.

8. Study and reflect on the prayers of the Bible.

9. Follow through on your resolve—*No decision made without prayer.*

10. Feed your heart and mind with God's Word.

Elizabeth George
A Woman's Call to Prayer

Video Notes

1. Time spent with prayer.
2. We must say no to things that are pleasant to make time for prayer.
2B. Daily Walk - Consult God
3. Daily desire - To walk with God
4. Commentment. R. 12:1
to all that you are - all that you have.

Week Three

A Heart for Discipline

"Something is better than nothing, so do something!"

A Heart for Discipline

"Something is better than nothing, so do something!"

Psalm 119:1-48; Mark 1:29-39; Galatians 5:16-26

Key Truths:

❖ Developing daily spiritual disciplines transforms how we think, act, and believe.

❖ Making room for time with God in already-busy schedules requires major adjustments and reordering our priorities.

❖ God's Word can change our priorities and fuel a greater passion for serving the Lord.

How do we become women after God's own heart? As we step into this new group of lessons we will focus on the "Yes, but how?" aspect of developing a heart for God. One chief component is a heart for discipline. How can we become a Paul, a David, a Hannah, a Mary—a person who looks to God's Word, prays with passion, and experiences God's multitudinous blessings? We must discipline ourselves to schedule, maintain, and protect a daily time with the Master, our Savior and Lord.

Crucial to maintaining a daily discipline is finding the best time, the best place, and the best plan for spending time with God. As you look closely at your daily routine, what is *your* best time, *your* best place, and *your* best plan for spending time with God?

Jesus' habit was to arise before dawn and spend time with His Father in prayer. Jesus also found a place for prayer that was away from others, a place where He would not be interrupted. Jesus and His disciples led noticeably different lives because they spent time daily in prayer.

We are in a tug of war with a world of competing values. We are besieged by marketers, assailed by cultural icons to adopt their shallow definitions of tolerance, and torn between God's call to holy living and the world's call to take care of number one. If we will develop a heart for discipline and allow the Lord to transform our hearts and minds, we can learn to live above the tumult and become women whose hope and faith draw others to the foot of the cross.

This week's verse to remember:

"Now in the morning, having risen a long while before daylight, He went out and departed to a solitary place; and there He prayed."

Mark 1:35 (NKJV)

Day One: Daily Discipline

Nehemiah 1:4-11; Luke 2:36-38; Mark 1:29-39

Hearing from God

1. Pull out your dictionary today, and look up the word "discipline." Write down the definition in the space below.

   _____

   _____

   _____

   _____

2. To become women after God's own heart, we must understand how much we need spiritual discipline in our busy lives. There is so much to do and so little time to do it! Take time to read the following scriptures. Jot down key words that describe each person's discipline in prayer.

   Nehemiah—Nehemiah 1:4-11 _____

   _____

   Daniel—Daniel 6:10 _____

   _____

   Jesus—Luke 22:39-40 _____

   _____

3. The prophetess Anna is an example of a woman after the heart of God. Read her story in Luke 2:36-38. Then respond to the following questions.

   A. List some of the excuses Anna could have made for not being in the temple that day. _____

   _____

   _____

   B. What spiritual disciplines did Anna practice on a regular basis? _____

   _____

   _____

   C. What blessings came to Anna because of her daily spiritual disciplines and God's grace? _____

   _____

   _____

4. Jesus' discipline of arising early to pray enhanced his ministry and strengthened His relationship with His Heavenly Father. Read Mark 1:29-39, and respond to the following questions.

   A. List some of the excuses Jesus could have made for not arising early to pray that day. _____

   _____

   _____

   B. In what way did Jesus' early morning time in prayer influence how He spent His day? _____

   _____

   _____

Responding to God: "Yes, but how?"

5. To develop a daily discipline of prayer, Bible study, and time with the Lord, you will need a plan. If you have not yet developed a plan or established a daily discipline that fits your life, fill out the following blueprint.

The Best Time: When is the best time of day for me to devote uninterrupted time to prayer, Bible study, and meditation?

❏ Before breakfast ❏ After breakfast ❏ After lunch ❏ Late afternoon

❏ After supper ❏ Late evening

The Best Place: Where is the best place for me to devote uninterrupted time to prayer, Bible study, and meditation?

❏ Bedroom ❏ Kitchen ❏ Living room/Den ❏ Bathroom ❏ Closet

❏ Other room: _____

The Best Plan: You will need a plan for organizing your Bible study, directing your prayer, and spending uninterrupted time meditating on God's Word. Jot down ideas on how you plan to approach each spiritual discipline.

My plan for Bible study: _____

_____

My plan for daily prayer: _____

_____

My plan for meditating on God's Word: _____

_____

> *Build yourself a cell in your heart, and retire there to pray.*
>
> **— Catherine of Siena —**

LifeScene

Jeanette was Mrs. Organization. She approached every task from a strategic point of view and gathered all of her resources accordingly. When it came to her daily quiet time, she designated her sewing room as her study. She had six sharpened pencils, two clean notepads, a three-ring binder, her Bible, a printed prayer guide, a timer, and a place to set her hot cup of coffee. She arose promptly at 5 AM daily and went directly to her assignment. After three months of faithful commitment to her quiet time, she was losing steam. She sensed no response from God, no message for her life. She became increasingly frustrated. Then she read an article in a devotional magazine that changed everything and transformed her quiet time.

What do you think she discovered in that article?

_____

_____

_____

_____

_____

_____

Summary

Faithful women and men of God make a practice of developing daily spiritual disciplines that transform the way they approach every day. Faithful attention to spiritual disciplines puts a believer in an ideal position to hear from the Lord and to receive His greatest blessings. We must develop a plan that will encourage us to spend time with God daily. Something is better than nothing, so do something and do it every day.

Today, Lord, I need your help and encouragement to develop a daily discipline of spending time with you. The prayer of my heart is

_____

_____

_____

_____

---

3 Simple Steps to a Daily Quiet Time

Determine a time — When will your time be? Once you select your time, protect it and keep it as if it is an appointment, because it is. This appointment with God is the most important appointment you will have all day.

Determine a place — Choose a location that is quiet, where you can be alone. Where will your place be?

Determine a plan — Use a notebook to organize your Bible study and prayer life. Do you have an idea for your plan?

Day Two: Daily Time

Psalm 119:1–48; Romans 12:1–2

Hearing from God

1. For most of us, too many days pass before we "pull off the road" and spend time with God. Life is so "daily" that we need daily time with God and His Word. Take time to read these scriptures, and then jot down a phrase that underscores the importance of daily time in God's Word.

   Deuteronomy 32:46–47 _____

   _____

   Joshua 1:8 _____

   _____

   Psalm 63:1 _____

   _____

   Isaiah 40:8 _____

   _____

   Matthew 6:33 _____

   _____

   2 Timothy 3:16–17 _____

   _____

2. Great blessings and endurance come to the woman who spends daily time with the Lord. Read Psalm 1, and jot down some of the blessings and benefits that come to those with a heart for the Lord.

_____
_____
_____

3. Psalm 119 is a series of timeless songs in praise of God's Word. Read several verses from this chapter, and copy a verse that challenges you to spend daily time in God's Word.

_____
_____
_____

4. Devoting an opportune time every day to spend with the Lord will require great sacrifice. Read Romans 12:1–2. What does the phrase "living sacrifice" say to you?

_____
_____
_____

Talent develops itself in solitude; the talent of prayer, of faith, of meditation, of seeing the unseen.

– Henry Drummond –

5. What blessings are promised to us if we offer ourselves as daily, living sacrifices, holy and pleasing to God?

_____
_____
_____
_____

Responding to God: "Yes, but how?"

6. What things, thoughts, and events tend to keep you from spending daily time in God's Word?

_____
_____
_____

7. What can you do about these things, thoughts, and events? How can you simplify your life—at least a little—to make room for daily time with God?

_____
_____
_____

8. To what can you say no so you can win back time from less worthy endeavors and devote more time to abiding in Christ?

_____
_____
_____
_____

LifeScene *Maria married someone just like her father, although she did not realize it at the time. Like her father, Bob rises early and expects a big, hot breakfast before he leaves for work. He also expects a clean house when he returns—even though Maria and Bob have three young, active children. Bob works hard at the office and makes a good living, and he expects Maria to work hard at home. Maria is a loyal wife and a hardworking mom, but it takes every ounce of energy for her to take care of her children and meet Bob's expectations. When someone encourages her to get up before the family and spend time with God, she just laughs and says, "No way."*

Is there "no way" for Maria, or is there a way? What are your thoughts?

_____

_____

_____

_____

_____

Summary

The value of spending time in God's Word is so great that believers need to adjust daily schedules to make room for God's truth. Every person faces daunting challenges in setting aside such time. Nearly everyone's schedule is hectic and demanding. Spending daily time with the Lord is one way we can offer ourselves as living sacrifices, holy and pleasing to God.

Father, I want to be a living sacrifice. Today the prayer of my heart is

_____

_____

_____

_____

There are three stages in Bible reading: (1) the cod liver oil stage when you take it like medicine; (2) the shredded wheat stage when it's nourishing but dry; and (3) the peaches and cream stage when it is consumed with passion and pleasure.

—Albert M. Wells—

Four Important Choices

1. **Choose to spend time with God.** This is your choice. If spending time with God in His Word and in prayer is important to you, then you will find the time. How do you think spending more time with God will increase your desire and passion?

2. **Choose God's ways at every opportunity.** Discipline is developed one choice at a time. As you make those moment-by-moment decisions to live according to God's principles, you will develop a heart for God.

3. **Commit yourself daily to God.** Is this a commitment you are ready to make today? Every day? It should be. If not, why?

4. **Cultivate a hot heart.** God desires that you and I develop a heart that is "hot." Read Revelation 3:15–16. How would you rate your heart condition?

Day Three: Daily Walk

Matthew 11:28–30; Galatians 5:16–26; 2 Corinthians 4:16–18

Hearing from God

1. Have you ever thought about the phrase "walking with Jesus"? What does this suggest to you? Jesus called His disciples to leave their jobs and follow Him. Read the following verses. Then beside each scripture reference, write what you think Jesus meant by His statements.

Matthew 4:18–20 _____

_____

Matthew 11:28–30 _____

_____

Matthew 16:24 _____

_____

2. Apollos was an educated man who studied God's Word and was effective in building New Testament churches. Read Acts 18:24–28. Note the phrase "the way of the Lord." How does anyone become intimately familiar with the way of the Lord?

_____

_____

_____

3. As you walk along your daily path, what does God's Word say is vitally important? Jot down God's answers to these questions after reading the following scriptures.

Jeremiah 17:7–8 _____

_____

Proverbs 4:14–27 _____

_____

Galatians 5:16–18 _____

_____

Galatians 5:22–26 _____

_____

4. Developing a heart for God through discipline is no easy task. Discouragement, setbacks, trials, and temptations block the way. But God's Word provides great encouragement. Read 2 Corinthians 4:16–18. How does this scripture encourage your heart today?

_____

_____

_____

_____

Heaven is not here, it's there. If we were given all we wanted here, our hearts would settle for this world rather than the next. God is forever luring us up and away from this one, wooing us to Himself and His still invisible Kingdom, where we will certainly find what we so keenly long for.

— Elisabeth Elliot —

Responding to God: "Yes, but how?"

5. Look up the word "priority" in your dictionary. Write the definition in the space that follows.

_____

_____

_____

_____

Good, better, best,

Never let it rest

Until your good is better,

And your better best.

6. Where does your relationship with God fit into your priorities?

_____

_____

7. If we as women say yes to everything that comes our way, we will eventually end up saying no to the things that matter most. Making your daily walk with God central to your life will mean saying yes or no to many good things. Take a moment to pray, asking the Lord to help you pause and pray before saying yes or no to life's many challenges.

8. To what degree is your walk with God influencing your decisions and choices in life?
   ❑ to a great extent   ❑ a little   ❑ not much   ❑ I really don't know.

9. If you want God's Spirit and His Word to have greater influence on your decisions and choices, jot down some ideas on how you can develop a closer walk with Christ daily.

_____

_____

_____

_____

_____

LifeScene   *Colleen is active in her weekday women's Bible study group. She helps maintain the group's newsletter. She brings food every week. She sends out prayer cards and other meeting reminders faithfully. Colleen feels good about her involvement and knows that the Lord will understand whenever she needs to take care of herself. To help meet her needs that often go unmet, Colleen spends considerable late-night time, after her husband goes to bed, in an Internet chat room, talking to other women—and occasionally men—who empathize with her life struggles. She is beginning to feel uneasy and uncomfortable with this new audience of "listeners."*

What's going on in her life? What is your advice?

_____

_____

_____

_____

_____

Summary

Walking daily with Christ means more than spending time in His Word and in prayer. Walking with Christ means making His way our way, His will our will, His thoughts our thoughts. Walking daily with Christ transforms our values and changes the way we think. As we walk through life, our decisions and our behavior should reflect the life of Jesus Christ, our Savior.

Today, Lord, I want to walk closely with You. The prayer of my heart is

_____

_____

_____

_____

Day Four: Daily Desire

1 Peter 2:1-3; Romans 7:8-20; Psalm 37:4

Hearing from God

1. Stop and listen to your heart. What is your heart's desire? What do you most hope for, pray for, and yearn for in life?

   _____

   _____

2. Destructive, selfish desires bring problems to our lives. When we act to squelch those desires and focus on the things of God, we will grow and mature in Christ. Read 1 Peter 2:1-3.

   What sins are lurking in our selfish desires? _____

   _____

   _____

   What does God say we should do about these sins? _____

   _____

   _____

   What does God command that we desire? _____

   _____

   _____

   What do you think Peter means by "pure spiritual milk"? _____

   _____

   _____

3. Some women believe that their desires are natural forces that spring up beyond their control. But our desires are really the product of what we choose to value, what we decide is most important. Read the following scriptures, and answer the question for each.

   Romans 7:8,18-20—How does sin affect our desires? _____

   _____

   _____

   Romans 10:1—What was Paul's desire for his race? _____

   _____

   _____

   1 Corinthians 14:1—What does Paul urge believers to desire? _____

   _____

   _____

   James 1:13-15—What is the ultimate result of giving in to selfish desire? _____

   _____

   _____

   2 Peter 2:10—How does our sinful nature respond to authority? _____

   _____

   _____

4. God's Word gives us hope for controlling and fulfilling our desires. Read these two scriptures, and jot down the hopeful truths you discover.

   Psalm 37:4 _____

   _____

   Philippians 2:12-13 _____

   _____

Responding to God: "Yes, but how?"

5. If you are actively trying to develop godly discipline in your life, jot down some steps you are taking or plans you are following to achieve this goal.

   _____

   _____

   _____

   _____

6. If you are struggling to develop godly discipline, consider seeking the counsel of another woman. Also ask her or another Christian friend to be your accountability and prayer partner. Read Ecclesiastes 4:9-12. Why is a Christian friend or a Christian spouse an aid to godly discipline?

   _____

   _____

   _____

   _____

The greatest hindrance to our spiritual development—indeed, the whole hindrance—is that we allow our passions and desires to control us, and we do not strive to walk in the perfect way of the saints. When we meet the least adversity, we are too quickly dejected and we turn to other people for comfort, instead of to God.

— Thomas à Kempis —

7. Read Titus 2:3–5. Meditate on this scripture for a moment; then answer the questions below.

What is this verse saying to you about your desires and role? _____

_____

_____

What avenue of service does this scripture open for you? _____

_____

_____

LifeScene *Sheila prided herself on being spontaneous. She believed in the spontaneity of the Holy Spirit and resisted efforts to "box in" God or overschedule spiritual experiences. Sheila believed that God was all-powerful and would direct her heart wherever He wanted her to go. As a result, Sheila was sometimes unpredictable, waiting until the last minute to commit to something. She would cancel appointments at the last moment so she could pursue something else that attracted her attention. Sheila refused to be fenced in and restricted by human schedules. She believed that she should always be free to "go with God."*

What do you think about Sheila's spiritual orientation? Is she a good model for other women? Why or why not?

_____

_____

_____

_____

_____

In my heart I do have a fear.... I long to grow more godly with each passing day. Call it "the fear of the Lord," being in awe of Him and scared to death of any sin that would mar my life at this point.

— Anne Ortlund —

Summary

Destructive, selfish desires bring problems to our lives. Our desires are a product of what we decide is important. God's Word gives us hope and direction for controlling our desires and seeking His kingdom first. Partnering with your Christian spouse or friend can help you transform your desires into a passion for pleasing and serving God.

Lord, I want You to direct my desires and strengthen my will. My prayer today is _____

_____

_____

Day Five: Daily Commitment

2 Samuel 24; Matthew 5:8; Romans 12:1-2

Hearing from God

1. Begin this lesson by stopping and thanking God for His great blessings in your life. Then take a moment to review the four daily disciplines we have studied thus far.

   Daily _____

   Daily _____

   Daily _____

   Daily _____

2. Every day we need to commit our lives to the Lord. All that we are, all that we have, and all that we can become must be given to the Lord daily. Read these scriptures, and note those parts of life that God calls us to commit to Him.

   Psalm 24:3-4 _____

   _____

   Psalm 34:12-13 _____

   _____

   Psalm 25:15 _____

   _____

   Psalm 63:8 _____

   _____

   Matthew 5:8 _____

   _____

   Romans 10:15 _____

   _____

   Romans 12:1-2 _____

   _____

   Philippians 1:20-21 _____

   _____

3. David, a man after God's own heart, failed and sinned throughout his life. One of David's sins was devastating to the nation of Israel. You can read about this event in 2 Samuel 24. Why did David insist on paying Araunah for the site and supplies needed for his sacrifice in 2 Samuel 24:18-25?

   _____

   _____

   _____

   _____

If God is with us and we're with Him, we have nothing to fear.

Remember the promises of God, and respond in faith.

365 Life Lessons from Bible People

4. In the early church, believers were so committed to the Lord that they gave generously of their possessions. Read Acts 2:42–47. What blessings did believers experience in those days?

_____

_____

_____

_____

Lord, I give up all my own plans and purposes, all my own desires and hopes, and accept Thy will for my life. I give myself, my time, my all utterly to Thee to be Thine forever. Fill me and seal me with Thy Holy Spirit. Use me as Thou wilt, send me where Thou wilt, work out Thy whole will in my life at any cost, now and forever.

— Betty Scott Stam —

Responding to God: "Yes, but how?"

5. Everything we commit to the Lord costs us something. A daily commitment of ourselves and all that we are comes at great cost. Is there any thing or any part of your being that you are reluctant to commit to the Lord? If so, list it in the space that follows. Be honest with God.

_____

_____

_____

6. Were you honest in your response? If so, stop and pray. Ask the Lord to help you grow in trusting Him. Ask Him to give you the will and desire to entrust all of yourself, all that you have, and all of your relationships to Him. After praying, write down any thoughts or images that came to mind while you were praying.

_____

_____

_____

7. I have a friend whose husband asked her to sign a commitment card that simply stated her complete surrender to the Lord. Take a moment to read this card. If you are willing to make this commitment, sign and date the card. You may want to cut this card out of your workbook and use it as a Bible bookmark or as a reminder by your bedside.

> *Anything.   Anywhere.*
> *Anytime.   At any cost.*
>
> Name _____
>
> Date _____

8. If God has been speaking to you about something He wants you to do and you have been putting it off or ignoring it, now is the time to respond in trust and commitment. Write down what you believe God has been saying to you, and act on it now.

_____

_____

_____

_____

LifeScene *Linda has learned a lot about herself during the first three weeks of this study. One painful self-revelation has been her tendency to start something and not finish it. God has been speaking to her through this study and calling her to a daily commitment, but she fears that she will commit herself and then drop out as she has before. She eagerly participates in the weekly sessions and the video, but in her heart she has a nagging doubt. She secretly wonders whether her faith in God is real and whether God has given up on her. You notice that she is unusually quiet today, and you ask her why. Reluctantly she shares her fear with you.*

How can you encourage and reassure her?

_____

_____

_____

_____

_____

Summary

Every day we need to commit our lives to the Lord. All that we are, all that we have, and all that we can become must be given to the Lord daily. A daily commitment of ourselves and all that we are comes at great cost. Give all of yourself, all that you have, and all of your relationships to Him.

Today, Lord, I commit all that I am and all that I have to You.
The prayer of my heart is _____

_____

_____

_____

Video Notes

Week Four

A Heart for Your Husband

"Helping, loving, submitting to, and respecting your mate"

Week Four

A Heart for Your Husband

"Helping, loving, submitting to, and respecting your mate"

Genesis 1:26-28; Proverbs 31:10-31; Ephesians 5:21-31

Key Truths:

✤ The help that a wife brings to her husband is the greatest asset in his life.

✤ Women who submit to their husbands present a powerful example of God's design for the church.

✤ A woman's closest friend should be her husband, and a man's closet friend, his wife.

What a joy it is to love our husbands (Titus 2:4)! The lessons that follow will help married women do just that.

God gives Christian wives four specific guidelines for their role in the marriage relationship. In the next few lessons, you'll discover these guidelines. But what if you aren't married? That's fine. Go ahead and take these lessons to heart. Knowing these guidelines will strengthen your knowledge of God's Word and help you to help others.

The last half of the twentieth century experienced a cultural earthquake in the attitudes of women toward their identity, roles, and relationships with others. So-called trendsetters encouraged women to free themselves from old concepts (translated "biblical truth") about a woman's role in marriage, the workplace, and the home. As a result, too many women today have lost a scriptural understanding of what marriage is all about and how vital a woman's role is in this most basic of all human relationships.

This week we will reexamine a woman's role as helper to her husband, and we will discover the inestimable value and blessing that a woman brings to a marriage. Another much-maligned word in our culture's lexicon is "submission." Yet the Bible shows us how a wife's submission to her husband is a powerful picture and example to the church of how the family of God is to submit to the lordship of Jesus Christ.

This week's verse to remember:

"And the LORD God said, 'It is not good that man should be alone; I will make him a helper comparable to him.'"

Genesis 2:18 (NKJV)

Perhaps the greatest key to a successful marriage is a woman's respect for her husband. Without it, marriages dissolve into predictable statistics. When a husband gains his wife's respect and lives with her respect, he is a greater shepherd, champion, and servant than he could possibly be otherwise. What is the secret to a lasting marriage and a powerful church? A woman's heart for her husband.

Day One: A Wife Is to Help Her Husband

Genesis 1:26–28; 2:18; Proverbs 31:10–31

Hearing from God

What a joy it is to love our husbands! Even if you are not married, this study will help you understand and interpret the role of a wife to others. Knowing God's guidelines will enrich your understanding of God's Word and equip you to minister to other women.

1. Read Genesis 2:18, and copy the verse in the space below.

_____

_____

_____

_____

2. One of woman's God-given roles is that of helper to her husband. Genesis 1:26–28 lists another role. Read this passage, and write down the role in the space below.

_____

_____

_____

_____

A helper has been defined as a help answering to him, or one who answers. She was to be one who could share man's responsibilities, respond to his nature with understanding and love, and wholeheartedly cooperate with him in working out the plan of God.

3. Contemporary American culture denigrates the woman who acknowledges her role as a helper to her husband. What other messages about marriage does our culture promote?

_____

_____

_____

_____

4. Read Proverbs 12:4 and 1 Corinthians 11:7. What do these passages say about a woman's great value and blessing?

_____

_____

_____

_____

5. Read Proverbs 31:10–31 about a wife of noble character. Then reread these verses, and list the things this woman does that directly or indirectly help her husband.

_____

_____

_____

_____

Responding to God: "Yes, but how?"

6. As you read these scriptures on a wife's role, what questions came to mind? Jot down a few.

_____

_____

_____

_____

A wife is a "helper" or "a help" as man's "counterpart." The wife becomes man's counterpart and companion.

Wycliffe Bible Commentary

7. One of the biggest obstacles to obeying God's instructions for wives is pride. Selfish pride afflicts men and women. Some women reject biblical teaching in this area, saying, "Wait a minute! I'm not about to let my husband walk all over me. I've got rights too." Read Philippians 2:1–8. How does the example of Jesus Christ serve as a model for women?

_____

_____

_____

_____

8. What adjustments, if any, do you need to make in your attitude as a wife and helper to your husband?

_____

_____

_____

_____

LifeScene

For several years Crystal has believed that God is punishing her for her sins as a teenager. Crystal married her childhood sweetheart right after graduating from high school, only to discover that he was not the man of her dreams. After the honeymoon Ron told Crystal he expected her to keep the house clean, never argue with his mother, and submit to his leadership. At first Crystal did not balk at Ron's expectations, because she thought he would help with household chores. But Ron settles back in his recliner after work every day and does nothing to help her. Even after several verbal firestorms, Ron refuses to budge. Day by day Crystal sinks lower and lower, convinced that she is doomed to a life of disappointment and despair. All joy has drained from her life, and she has now dropped out of your Sunday School class.

As her friend and fellow class member, what can you do?

_____

_____

_____

_____

Summary

One of woman's God-given roles is that of helper to her husband. A wife is a husband's crown and the glory of man. A noble, godly wife brings great honor and prestige to her husband and her family. She brings security and value to her home. Her worth, her value is far beyond financial estimation.

Today, Lord, as a woman and a wife, the prayer of my heart is

_____

_____

_____

_____

Day Two: A Wife Is to Submit to Her Husband

Ephesians 5:21–31; 1 Peter 2:13–15

Hearing from God

1. God's Word often speaks about submission and gives many reasons for submitting. Read these scriptures, and jot down the reasons believers should submit to the Lord and to others.

   Romans 13:1–3 _____

   _____

   Ephesians 5:21 _____

   _____

   James 4:1–10 _____

   _____

   Hebrews 13:17 _____

   _____

   1 Peter 2:13–15 _____

   _____

2. When a wife submits to her husband, she fulfills a vital biblical function that influences how people view God's Word. Read Titus 2:5, and write down the influence a wife has.

   _____

   _____

   _____

   _____

What does it mean to submit? It means to bend, to fit him, to suit him, to fit in with his life or plans, to adapt to his way, to subordinate yourself to him and his leadership. It means "no resistance."

3. Scripture gives additional insight into the value of submission. Read Colossians 3:18, and copy the verse below.

_____

_____

_____

_____

4. Ephesians 5 provides an extensive comparison between the husband-wife relationship and the relationship of the church to Jesus Christ. Read verses 21–33, and then answer the questions below.

How is a wife to submit to her husband? _____

How is a wife's submission like a church's submission? _____

_____

What impact do you think a host of godly women could have on their church

if they modeled biblical submission in their marriages? _____

_____

_____

5. Timothy's mother, Eunice, was married to a man who was Greek and probably not a believer. Yet Eunice and Timothy's grandmother Lois had a profound influence on Timothy's life. Read 2 Timothy 1:5. How do you think Eunice was able to submit to her unbelieving husband and still raise Timothy to have faith in Christ?

_____

_____

_____

_____

Responding to God: "Yes, but how?"

6. Our culture mocks the idea of wives submitting to their husbands and offers no support for the biblical model of submission in marriage. Do you have a model of healthy biblical submission in your life? If so, who serves as that model, and what have you learned from watching her?

_____

_____

_____

_____

7. Do you think a wife is free not to submit to her husband if he is not a believer? Explain your response, and refer to scriptures that support your answer.

_____

_____

_____

_____

Submitting to another person is an often misunderstood concept. It does not mean becoming a doormat. Christ—at whose name "every knee shall bow in heaven and on earth and under the earth"—submitted His will to the Father, and we honor Christ by following His example. When we submit to God, we become more willing to obey His command to submit to others, that is, to subordinate our rights to theirs. For a wife this means willingly following her husband's leadership in Christ.

— Neil S. Wilson —

8. If submitting to your husband seems beyond your ability or desire at this time, take a moment to ask the Lord to speak to your heart. Read the supreme example of submission in Matthew 26:36–46. How can a wife inspire her husband to be a stronger spiritual leader in the home?

_____

_____

_____

_____

LifeScene

Brenda rushes in her parents' house in tears. After one month with her new husband, Alan, Brenda is ready to leave him. Brenda's parents always allowed her to maintain her own checking account, but Alan insists on one joint checking account. Alan prepared a budget that severely limits the discretionary money Brenda can spend. Alan wants to wait two years before they have children, and Brenda had been counting on starting a family right away. Alan also insists that he and Brenda will spend every Christmas with his parents in a distant state. The more Brenda talks to her parents, the angrier her father becomes. He sides with Brenda and is ready to call Alan and give Alan a piece of his mind.

As Brenda's mother and the wife of her father, what do you say?

_____

_____

_____

_____

Summary

God's Word speaks often about submission and gives many reasons for submitting. When a wife submits to her husband, she fulfills a vital biblical function that influences how people view God's Word. Our culture mocks the idea of wives submitting to their husbands, but God's Word is clear on this matter. Jesus Christ offers men and women a supreme example of submission.

Today, Lord, I submit myself to You. The prayer of my heart is _____

_____

_____

_____

Day Three: A Wife Is to Respect Her Husband

Song of Solomon 5:10–16; Ephesians 5:33; 1 Peter 3:6

Hearing from God

1. We have studied two of four biblical instructions that God has given to wives. Before we move to the third instruction, list the first two that you have studied thus far.

    A wife is to _____

    A wife is to _____

2. Read Ephesians 5:33 (printed in the right margin), and fill in the blanks in the paraphrase below.

    A husband must _____ his wife as he _____ himself,

    and a wife must _____ her husband.

3. Look up the definition of "respect" in your dictionary, and copy it in the space below.

    _____

    _____

    _____

    _____

4. In typically honest fashion, the Bible depicts the success and failure of wives in respecting their husbands. Read the following scriptures, and jot down how biblical wives did or did not respect their husbands.

    Michal in 2 Samuel 6:16 _____

    _____

    The wife in Proverbs 31:12 _____

    _____

    Gomer in Hosea 3:1–3 _____

    _____

    Sarah in 1 Peter 3:6 _____

    _____

5. Song of Solomon 5:10–16 is a poem of praise from a wife to her husband. Read this scripture, and note below how this wife shows respect for her husband.

    _____

    _____

    _____

    _____

Nevertheless let each one of you in particular so love his own wife as himself, and let the wife see that she respects her husband.

Ephesians 5:33 (NKJV)

Week Four

Responding to God: "Yes, but how?"

6. Often after years of marriage, a husband and wife lose esteem for one another. Familiarity, flaws, and failures convince us that the person we married is not as special as we once thought. A common casualty in marriage is mutual respect. Another common mistake is a wife's decision to withhold respect for her husband until he starts respecting her. Yet God's Word does not allow a wife to set conditions for respecting her husband. If showing respect for your husband is difficult for you, briefly explain why.

_____

_____

_____

_____

7. If respecting your husband is going to take some effort, the place to begin is prayer. Withholding respect is difficult when you are praying for that person. Commit yourself right now to begin praying for your husband every day. Here are some areas you can address in your prayer.

- *His health*
- *His success in his job*
- *His relationship with Christ*
- *His wisdom and discernment*
- *His love for Christ's church*
- *His roles as husband, father, son, brother*
- *His dreams and goals in life*
- *His willingness to serve the Lord*
- *His joy in life*
- *His healing for past hurts and grief*
- *His love for you*

Place a **paper clip** on this page so you can return to it daily when you pray. As you pray for your husband, the Lord will work in your husband's life and in yours.

8. Regardless of how long you have been married, you know your husband well. What two or three things could you do or change that would show respect for your husband? Think for a moment, and then make some notes below.

1. _____

2. _____

3. _____

LifeScene

Rosa married Jim two months after graduating from high school. Before she knew it, Jim buried himself in his job. He worked twelve to fifteen hours a day. At first Rosa thought Jim would let up on his workaholic schedule after he got a promotion, but Jim never cut back. As Rosa got to know Jim's parents better, she saw the same pattern in Jim's father. Jim's mother was a proud woman who thought the universe revolved around her. She was often caustic and demeaning to Jim. No matter what Jim accomplished, his mother found a way to minimize it. Rosa feels increasingly estranged from Jim. She spends most of her day away from him, and when he is home, he acts tired and distant. Jim seems oblivious to Rosa's emotional state. Your sister Rosa calls you late one night and cries her heart out about her failing marriage.

You listen for a long time, and then you say...

_____

_____

_____

_____

Summary

God commands wives to respect their husbands just as He commands husbands to love their wives. These commands are unconditional. Often after years of marriage, a husband and wife lose esteem for each other. Through prayer and obedience to God's Word, a wife can respect her husband in ways that honor God and fulfill His command.

Today, Lord, the prayer of my heart is _____

_____

_____

_____

_____

Day Four: A Wife Is to Love Her Husband

Genesis 2:24; Proverbs 27:6–10; Titus 2:3–5

Hearing from God

1. We read Titus 2:3–5 earlier in our study, but take a moment to read it again. List at least five things that older women are called to teach to younger women:

    1. _____
    2. _____
    3. _____
    4. _____
    5. _____

2. The love that women are to have for their husbands, as described in this passage, is *phileo* love. *Phileo* love is a friendship love. This *phileo* love says, "I love you. I love being with you. I love being your friend. You are my best friend." Women are often better at friendships than men are. Read the following scriptures, and write down what friends do for one another.

    Exodus 33:11 _____

    _____

    Psalm 35:14 _____

    _____

    Psalm 41:9 _____

    _____

    Psalm 55:13–14 _____

    _____

    Proverbs 17:17 _____

    _____

Proverbs 18:24 _____

_____

Proverbs 27:6–10 _____

_____

Ecclesiastes 4:10_____

_____

> *The point at which many marriages jump the track is in over-investing in children and under-investing in the marriage.*
>
> **Howard and Charlotte Clinebell**

3. Another way a wife can develop a heart of love for her husband is to make her relationship with him her number-one human relationship. Read Genesis 2:24 and Matthew 19:5. What relationships need to be subordinated to the marriage relationship?

_____

_____

4. Read Genesis 24:42–59. Why do you think Rebekah chose to leave her family and marry Isaac without even meeting him?

_____

_____

_____

_____

Responding to God: "Yes, but how?"

5. What have you done with your husband lately that has added to your friendship?

_____

_____

_____

_____

6. Sometimes a tension exists between honoring your parents and loving and respecting your husband. If you have ever experienced this tension, describe that time and how you resolved the tension.

_____

_____

_____

_____

7. As you think about the levels of relationship you have with your husband (e.g., romantic, sexual, parental, friendship), what changes do you need to make to develop further a heart of love for your husband?

_____

_____

_____

_____

LifeScene *Angela and Ron have built a successful and smooth-running home. Their three kids feel secure and loved. Things are hectic at home, but schedules are met, and family members are rarely late for appointments or sports practice. Weeks and months fly by like speedboats, but Angela and Ron have perfected home life so the family can ride the waves and keep their heads above water. If this family were a corporation, stockholders would be earning great dividends. Angela is restless, however, and she feels increasingly empty and depressed. Unknown to her, Ron is experiencing similar emotions. Subtle temptations are arising that could be deadly to their marriage.*

What are some of these temptations, and how can Angela and Ron overcome them?

_____

_____

_____

Summary

A wife needs to love her husband in many ways, including being his closest, most loyal friend. By devoting herself to increasing the friendship she and her husband share, a wife can strengthen her heart for her husband. Placing her relationship with her husband above all other human relationships is foundational to a successful marriage and a primary way a wife expresses love for her husband.

Today, Lord, help me to be my husband's best friend and to strengthen my heart of love for him by _____

_____

_____

Day Five: Yes, but How?

Proverbs 31:10–31; 1 Corinthians 7:3–5

Hearing from God

1. As we near the end of this great week of study, take a moment to review the four biblical instructions that God has given to wives.

   A wife is to _____

   A wife is to _____

   A wife is to _____

   A wife is to _____

2. Today's lesson will focus on practical ways to love your husband. Read the scriptures below. Draw a line from each scripture reference to the correct action listed in the right column.

Proverbs 12:25	Be kind to him
Proverbs 21:5	Respect him
Proverbs 31:15	Physically love him
Romans 12:10	Prepare for him daily
1 Corinthians 7:3–5	Praise him
James 5:16	Pray always
Ephesians 5:33	Pray for him daily
Ephesians 6:18	Honor him
Titus 2:4	Plan for him daily

3. Let's return once more to Proverbs 31 to see how a wife is to love her husband. Note the impact of a godly, noble wife on her husband's life and behavior. Read the following verses, and jot down the central thought or teaching of each scripture.

v. 10 _____

v. 11 _____

v. 12 _____

v. 23 _____

vv. 28–29 _____

Responding to God: "Yes, but how?"

4. Take a look at the practical actions listed in question 2. Think about each action based in scripture, and jot down one or two ways you can implement these teachings in your home.

Be kind to him. _____

_____

Respect him. _____

_____

Physically love him. _____

_____

Prepare for him daily. _____

_____

Praise him. _____

_____

Pray always. _____

_____

Pray for him daily. _____

_____

Honor him. _____

_____

Plan for him daily. _____

_____

God's recipe for a happy marriage contains four basic ingredients—a helping hand, a submissive spirit, a respectful manner, and a loving heart.

— Elizabeth George —

5. Sometimes the noble woman in Proverbs 31 seems superhuman, unreal, and impossible. She gets up before dawn. She is never idle. She buys land and plants a vineyard. She manages a business and earns a profit. She helps the poor and needy. She never worries about tomorrow.

You may believe you have little in common with such a woman, but you really do. You have the same twenty-four-hour day she had. Through Christ, all things are possible. The best way to develop a heart for your husband is to look forward and not behind, to plan to make the best of each day rather than allow a new day to overwhelm you.

Take a moment to look at your schedule for next week. What adjustments are needed to free the time to be a woman with a heart for God and for your husband? Write down your thoughts, and then incorporate your ideas into your calendar and schedule.

_____

_____

_____

_____

_____

_____

LifeScene *Melissa's parents were well-known philanthropists in the community. Life in her family was often focused on public service, charities, and community causes. Melissa is dedicated to being a Proverbs 31 woman. She serves as PTA president at her daughter's school, homeroom mom in her son's fifth-grade classroom, secretary of the Junior League, and chairwoman of the annual fund-raiser for the children's hospital. Her husband and children complain that she is never home, but Melissa sees that they always have food on the table and clean clothes to wear. She gets up early and works hard every day. In spite of her efforts, her husband and children complain that their needs are going unmet. She tells them that they are being selfish, that they need to grow up and be more self-sufficient.*

Who's right? Who's wrong? And why? Where is the balance?

_____

_____

_____

_____

Summary

Developing a heart for your husband requires knowing God's Word and applying it to everyday life. Obedience to God's Word brings great rewards, but knowing how to obey is not always easy. Seek God's wisdom and discernment daily as you become a woman after God's own heart.

Lord, grant me wisdom and determination to obey Your Word.
Today the prayer of my heart is _____

_____

_____

_____

_____

Video Notes

Week Five

A Heart for Your Children

"Dedicating, teaching, and loving your children"

Week Five

A Heart for Your Children

"Dedicating, teaching, and loving your children"

1 Samuel 2:1-10; Proverbs 1:8; 6:20; Luke 1-2

Key Truths:

❖ Nurturing a child's faith in God is a vital role of every mother.

❖ When a mother dedicates her child to the Lord, she commits to pray and provide maximum exposure for her child to the things and people of God.

❖ Choosing to love our children—in spite of their natural-born selfish drives— is a choice that honors God and blesses a generation.

Onto whom should a woman's full heart overflow? If she is married, Titus 2:4 says her husband should be first to benefit from his wife's vital relationship with God through Jesus Christ. Then where? If she is a mother, Titus 2:4 says that her children are to be the next recipients of her joy, energy, and efforts. And the lessons that follow will help mothers do just that!

God gives Christian mothers specific guidelines for their role as moms. In the next few lessons, you'll discover these guidelines. And what if you aren't married or don't have children? Again, that's fine. Go ahead and take these lessons to heart. Knowing these guidelines will strengthen your knowledge of God's Word and enable you to help moms in your church, at work, in organizations where you volunteer, or perhaps even on the mission field.

When you stop to consider a mother's far-reaching influence in the lives of her children, overestimating her imprint is almost impossible. A woman after God's own heart knows her calling to teach her children the Word of God. This task of opening and explaining the words breathed by God leaves an eternal footprint not just in a child but also in our world. A noble, godly woman knows the high calling of her teaching.

This week's verse to remember:

"My son, hear the instruction of your father, And do not forsake the law of your mother."

Proverbs 1:8 (NKJV)

Women also help their children gain much-needed practical wisdom for successful living, living that truly pleases God. Just as Hannah dedicated her firstborn, Samuel, to the Lord's service, we, too need to dedicate our children to the Lord for His purposes and blessing. A woman who loves her children invests the best years of their lives and hers in bringing them up to know the Creator who made man, woman, marriage, and eternity.

Day One: A Mother Is to Teach Her Children Divine Law

Psalm 127:3–5; Proverbs 1:8; Isaiah 55:11

Hearing from God

1. God gives mothers guidance for their role as moms. Regardless of whether or not you are a mother, you will gain a greater understanding of God's Word by giving yourself fully to this week's study. What is the role of a mother according to Proverbs 1:8?

   _____

   _____

2. Reading and teaching God's Word to your child will have an enduring impact on his or her life. God's Word makes a difference. Read these scriptures, and identify the impact that God's Word can have on someone's life, especially a child's life.

   Isaiah 55:11 _____

   _____

   Romans 10:17 _____

   _____

   2 Timothy 3:15 _____

   _____

3. Understanding God's perspective on children is a crucial first step in having a heart for your child. Read the following scriptures, and jot down the truths you discover.

   Genesis 33:5 _____

   _____

   1 Samuel 1:5 _____

   _____

   Psalm 113:9 _____

   _____

   Psalm 127:3–5 _____

   _____

What is a godly mother? A godly mother is one who loves the Lord her God with all her heart, soul, mind, and strength and then passionately, consistently, and unrelentingly teaches her child to do the same.

*— **Elizabeth George** —*

4. The Bible pictures a mother's love for her children through the stories of several families. Read the following scriptures, and identify what you learn about each mother's heart for her child or children.

Sarah in Genesis 21:1-7 _____

_____

Rachel in Genesis 30:1 _____

_____

Hannah in 1 Samuel 1:5, 11-17, 24-28 _____

_____

5. Several mothers in the Bible taught their children the Word of God. Read the following scriptures, and note the evidence that these men learned God's Word from their mothers.

Luke 1:5-25, 57-80_____

_____

Luke 2:39-52 _____

_____

2 Timothy 1:5 _____

_____

Responding to God: "Yes, but how?"

6. In Deuteronomy 6:1-9, Moses instructed mothers and fathers to teach their children the Word of God, His decrees, and commands. Read this passage, and then list practical ways you can do the same with your children.

A. _____

B. _____

C. _____

D. _____

7. Think for a moment about what you want your child to understand about God, Jesus, the Holy Spirit, and faith. Write down simple statements of the truths you want to teach your child.

_____

_____

_____

_____

8. How can you begin teaching these truths to your children now, regardless of their ages?

_____

_____

_____

_____

∽

A Time to Decide

Decide that it is important to make time for teaching your children the Word of God.

Decide to turn off the television and pick up the Bible or a Bible storybook or activity book.

Decide that you will speak constantly of the Lord.

Decide what verses you and your children will memorize together.

∽

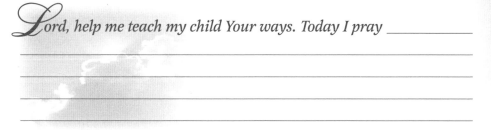

LifeScene — *Janelle is a busy single mother. Each day demands every ounce of energy she has to get her children ready for school, feed them breakfast, get them on the school bus, get dressed for work, work a full day at the office, return home and fix dinner, clean the kitchen, and get the children in bed. After she drops off her kids at church on Sunday, she rushes home to wash clothes and find a moment for herself before church is over. She believes the church will give them the spiritual instruction they need. When one of her children's Sunday School teachers calls Janelle and invites her to church, Janelle thanks her but says that church is a luxury she cannot afford.*

You are that Sunday School teacher. How do you respond?

_____

_____

_____

_____

Summary

God gives mothers guidance for their important duty as moms. Teaching their children the Word of God and nurturing faith in their young lives are vital roles for mothers. Reading and teaching God's Word to your child will have an enduring impact on his or her life. Even the best Sunday School or church cannot replace a mother's instruction in God's Word.

Lord, help me teach my child Your ways. Today I pray _____

_____

_____

_____

_____

Day Two: A Mother Is to Teach Her Children Practical Wisdom

Proverbs 2; 6:20; 22:6; Ephesians 6:1–2

Hearing from God

1. Practical wisdom is teaching based on God's Word. Practical wisdom provides believers with the principles, counsel, discernment, and practices they need to live in a way that pleases God. The following scriptures give insight into a mother's teaching role: Proverbs 6:20; 22:6; 31:1, 26. Read all of these scriptures, and then write a statement that captures the truths you have read.

_____

_____

_____

_____

2. As a mother, you can teach practical wisdom that addresses many areas of your child's life. Read these scriptures, and jot down the subjects that your child needs to learn.

   Proverbs 12:22 _____

   _____

   Proverbs 14:23 _____

   _____

   Proverbs 29:11 _____

   _____

   Ephesians 4:32 _____

   _____

   Ephesians 6:1 _____

   _____

   Ephesians 6:2 _____

   _____

There is no nobler career than that of motherhood at its best.... There is no higher height to which humanity can attain than that occupied by a converted, heaven-inspired, praying mother.

He who teaches the Bible is never a scholar; he is always a student.

3. Proverbs 2 lists the great benefits and rewards that come from accepting and applying God's practical wisdom. Included in this chapter are the blessings that will come to your child when he or she learns God's truth from you. List some of the blessings in store for your child.

   _____

   _____

   _____

   _____

4. Paul's advice to Timothy in Colossians 4:6 applies to mothers, too.

   Let your conversation be always full of grace, seasoned with salt, so that you may know how to answer everyone.

   What does this scripture say to you about how you talk, teach, and respond to your child? Ponder this question before writing your response.

   _____

   _____

   _____

   _____

Responding to God: "Yes, but how?"

5. Do you think that God's practical wisdom is the same thing as common sense? Explain your answer.

   _____

   _____

   _____

   _____

6. Our actions speak louder than our words. We may teach our children not to lie and then in their presence lie to someone or do something dishonest. To what degree is your life in harmony with what you want to teach your child? How well do you "walk your talk"? Circle your response.

   I seldom do what I teach my child.

   I sometimes walk my talk.

   I walk my talk.

7. If your life is not modeling what you want to teach your child, pause a moment in this workbook exercise. In an attitude of prayer, read Psalms 139 and 51. Confess your sins and failures to the Lord. Ask Him to make you sensitive to issues of integrity in your life and to prompt you whenever you need to make a change. **Pause and do this now.**

LifeScene Christy is a godly mother who takes her children to church and teaches them Bible truths at home. Her husband, Kyle, believes church is for women and children and never attends with his family. Kyle's employer is downsizing, which puts increasing demands on him to meet his sales quota. As stress at the office intensifies, Kyle often releases his anger on Christy and the children. His drinking and cursing have gotten out of control lately. Even the children can tell when Kyle is lying to them. Everything that Christy is trying to instill in her children seems to be undone when their father comes home. At first she tried to make excuses for Kyle, but she has run out of excuses. Her children are starting to question what Christy has been teaching them, and her son has started using some of his father's language.

What can Christy do?

_____

_____

_____

_____

Summary

Mothers are responsible for teaching God's practical wisdom to their children. Practical wisdom provides believers with the principles, counsel, discernment, and practices needed to live in a way that pleases God. Children who accept such teaching will receive vast blessings and benefits throughout their lives.

Today, Lord, the prayer of my heart is _____

_____

_____

_____

Day Three: A Mother Is to Dedicate Her Children

Proverbs 31:2; 1 Samuel 2:1–10; Luke 1:46–55

Hearing from God

1. As we continue this week to study a mother's role in developing a heart for her children, take a moment to review the two previous lessons. What two teaching assignments are given to mothers in God's Word?

   A mother is to teach her children _____

   A mother is to teach her children _____

2. Another call for mothers is found in Proverbs 31:2. Read this scripture, and fill in the missing words below.

   "O my son, O son of my womb, O son of _____."

3. The phrase you wrote in question 2 above refers to one who is dedicated to the Lord. We use many words today without fully understanding their meaning. Look up the word "dedicate" in your dictionary, and write the definition below.

   _____

   _____

   _____

   _____

> *You, dear mother—and grandmother—are on assignment from God to pray for your children. You may be the only person on the face of the earth who is! And if you aren't, then probably no one is!*
>
> — **Elizabeth George** —

4. You have already studied the example of Hannah, Samuel's mother. She dedicated Samuel to the Lord and fulfilled her vow to "give him to the LORD for all the days of his life" (1 Sam. 1:11). Take a moment to read Hannah's prayer of praise found in 1 Samuel 2:1–10. After reading this passage, compare Hannah's prayer to Mary's *Magnificat,* found in Luke 1:46–55. How are the two prayers similar?

   _____

   _____

   _____

   _____

   _____

5. Hannah's devotion to her son continued beyond his initial dedication. Read 1 Samuel 2:18–21, and describe Hannah's continuing devotion.

   _____

   _____

   _____

   _____

6. The entire nation of Israel was blessed through Samuel's dedication to the Lord. How was Hannah also blessed by her dedication of Samuel (see 1 Samuel 2:20–21)?

_____

_____

_____

_____

Responding to God: "Yes, but how?"

7. Two ways mothers dedicate their children to the Lord are through prayer and through providing maximum exposure to the things and people of God. Have you dedicated your children to the Lord through prayer?

❏ Yes   ❏ No   ❏ I don't know.

Are you fearful of dedicating your children to the Lord?

❏ Yes   ❏ No   ❏ I don't know.

If you have never dedicated your children to the Lord, stop and pray for each them. As difficult as it may be or as fearful as you may be to make such a dedication, give your children back to the Lord in prayer.

8. What are you currently doing to provide maximum exposure for your child to the things and people of God? Check each of the following statements that are true for your child.

❏ My child attends our church weekly.

❏ My child is part of a children's or youth Sunday School group.

❏ My child participates in our family devotions at home.

❏ My child is encouraged to conduct his or her own daily quiet time with God.

❏ My child has Christian friends.

> *Motherly training and dedication [provide] the first imparting of religious instruction, the solemn dedication of her child to the service of God, [and] repeated and earnest prayer on his behalf. Her child is not only her offspring; he is "the son of her vows," the one on whom she has expended her most fervent piety.*
>
> —*Author Unknown*—

LifeScene

Betty Kate suffered three miscarriages before her son, Brad, was born. She and her husband, Tim, praised God for Brad and dedicated him to the Lord. Since Brad was their only child, Betty Kate devoted herself tirelessly to raising and caring for him. She and Tim gave Brad anything necessary to make him happy. He was their pride and joy. They took him to church every Sunday and trusted him with freedoms and privileges that most children did not have. Occasionally when Brad got into trouble, Betty Kate and Tim bailed him out. One fateful night Brad and a carload of his friends were drinking and crashed into a tree, killing Brad and two other teens. Betty Kate fell into a black pit of shock and denial. Brad had been her life. She had dedicated him to the Lord.

What went wrong in this Christian family and what might help them?

_____

_____

_____

_____

Summary

A mother is to dedicate her children to the Lord. Two ways mothers dedicate their children are through prayer and through maximum exposure to the things and people of God.

Lord, I dedicate my child to You. Today the prayer of my heart is

_____

_____

_____

_____

Day Four: A Mother Is to Love Her Children

Genesis 25:27; 27:1-38; Luke 7:11-15

Hearing from God

1. We looked at Titus 2:3-5 and discovered that the first thing older women are to teach younger women is to love their husbands. What is the second thing older women are to teach?

   _____

   _____

2. King Solomon was challenged to prove which of two prostitutes was a child's true mother. Read 1 Kings 3:15-28. How was a mother's love for her child instrumental in revealing her identity?

   _____

   _____

   _____

   _____

3. Can a mother's love ever be a dangerous thing? Read Genesis 25:27 and 27:1-38, and identify the tragedy that resulted from a mother's partiality. Describe in the space below what went wrong in this family.

   _____

   _____

   _____

   _____

4. We have already studied the noble woman of Proverbs 31. Read verses 10-31 again, and list the ways a woman of God expresses her love for her children.

   _____

   _____

   _____

   _____

5. Jesus knew the depth of a mother's love for her son. Read Luke 7:11–15, and describe how Jesus responded to a loving mother's grief.

_____

_____

_____

_____

Responding to God: "Yes, but how?"

6. Studying a lesson on loving your children may seem unnecessary. What mother does not love her children? However, the news in our nation is full of stories of mothers who do not love their children. What current events come to your mind that bear out this disturbing fact?

_____

_____

_____

_____

7. Our children know how to provoke us, push us, and drive us to the brink. Some children seem born to oppose us at every step. Choosing to love our children in spite of their selfish bent honors the Lord. If you are struggling to know how best to love your children, describe your struggle in the space below. Write it, however, as a prayer to the Lord.

Heavenly Father, _____

_____

_____

_____

_____

8. When does loving your child cross the line and become spoiling your child? And how do you spoil a child anyway?

_____

_____

_____

_____

9. Review what you have learned in this lesson. What changes are needed in the way you show love for your children?

_____

_____

_____

_____

The mother's yearning, that completest type of the life in another life which is the essence of real human love, feels the presence of the cherished child even in the debased, degraded man.

— **George Eliot** —

LifeScene *Maria's daughter Candace loves the circus. Every year when the circus comes to town, Maria takes Candace and her friends to see the elephants, tigers, clowns, and trapeze artists. Now that Candace is in the third grade, Maria has been teaching Candace the importance of helping her with household chores before she goes outside to play. Candace, a strong-willed child, resists Maria's limits and likes to see what she can get away with. Last week Maria told Candace that if she did not complete her chores every day for three consecutive days, Maria would not take her to the circus. Candace did her chores well for two days and then did nothing the third day. When the circus opened, Maria told Candace why they would not be going to the circus this year. Candace cried and bargained but to no avail. Candace ran to her room, slammed the door, and cried herself to sleep. Maria cried too.*

Is Maria a loving mother? Why or why not?

_____

_____

_____

_____

Summary

A mother is to love her children, but the 24/7 responsibility of parenting can turn a loving mother into a vegetable! Selfishness and fatigue can tempt mothers to put anything and everything before their children. Choosing to love our children in spite of their selfish bent honors the Lord.

Today, Lord, help me truly love my child by _____

_____

_____

_____

Day Five: Yes, but How?

1 Samuel 1–2; Ruth 1–2; Luke 1–2

Hearing from God

1. I am so glad you have made it to this final lesson on developing a heart for your children. Before we focus on ways we can apply what we have learned this week, take a moment to review the four previous lessons by completing the following statements from each day.

   A mother is to _____

   A mother is to _____

   A mother is to _____

   A mother is to _____

2. Which of these four lessons has been most convicting to you as a mother? Why?

_____

_____

_____

_____

3. What is most meaningful to you about the lives of famous mothers in the Bible?

Sarah (Genesis 17:15–19; 18:11–15; 21:1–7) _____

_____

_____

Hannah (1 Samuel 1–2) _____

_____

_____

Naomi (Ruth 1–2) _____

_____

_____

Elizabeth (Luke 1:1–45) _____

_____

_____

Mary (Luke 1:26–2:51; John 2:1–11; 19:25–30) _____

_____

_____

4. Reread Proverbs 31:15–30. List the things you have in common with this mother in Proverbs.

_____

_____

_____

_____

5. If you see something in Proverbs 31 that you need to add to your life as a mother, list that trait or action in the following space.

_____

_____

_____

_____

I have a mother who prays for me and pleads with the Lord every day for me. Oh what a difference it makes for me—I have a mother who prays.

—Author Unknown—

> *The world is tugging at our children's hearts, pulling them down and away from God. Loving our children means we are willing to get down in the trenches and fight to turn our children's hearts toward God—toward His Word and His ways.*
>
> — **Elizabeth George** —

Responding to God: "Yes, but how?"

6. In the left column below, describe the mother you want to be to your children. If you are a grandmother, describe the relationship you want to have with your adult children and your grandchildren. In the right column below, list the changes you will need to make to be the mother or grandmother you want to be. After you finish, pray about the changes you have listed.

The Mother I Want to Be	Changes I Need to Make

LifeScene

Abby gets exasperated every time her mother, Vivian, comes to visit. Abby has two young children, one in school and another in day care. As a working mom, Abby is torn between her job and fulfilling all of her duties as a wife and mother. Vivian stayed at home with Abby and her siblings during Abby's childhood and never had to work outside the home. When Vivian comes for a visit, she lectures Abby about staying home with the children, and Abby ends up feeling guilty. Abby and her mother argue about this subject every time Vivian comes. Abby talks to you about the idea of not inviting her mother to visit anymore because the visits end up in heated arguments.

What do you say? What words of advice do you have?

_____

_____

_____

_____

_____

Summary

God's Word gives mothers inspiration and guidance for loving their children. No woman is capable of being the perfect mom, but God is rich in grace and able to forgive us when we fail. Seek the Lord's guidance and strength as you fulfill your high calling as a mother after God's own heart.

Father, I want to be a loving, godly mother to my children. Today the prayer of my heart is _____

_____

_____

Video Notes

Week Six

A Heart for Your Home

"Building, watching over, and keeping your home"

Week Six

A Heart for Your Home

"Building, watching over, and keeping your home"

Proverbs 24:3-4; Ephesians 5:15-16; Titus 2:4-5

Key Truths:

❖ A woman can build her home with godly wisdom or destroy it through foolish choices.

❖ Idleness or inattention to family needs breaks down the much-needed wall of love and security in the home.

❖ Tuning out distractions and tuning in to God's Word empowers women to manage their homes to the glory of God and the joy of their families.

Join me for a moment on a walk Jim and I once took through the streets of Old Jerusalem. Crowds of people—and animals!—were everywhere. The market was filled with hanging slabs of raw, fly-covered meat as well as other live, smelly, and noisy animals. Buses were belching fumes and dropping off tourists while dump trucks contributed their own clamor and diesel smells. The sound of construction rose with the relentless midday heat, and I had an incredible thirst (and headache!) building up with no relief in sight.

It was then that our guide, Bill, led us through one of the many closed doors that line the streets of the Old City and right into paradise! In a single moment we found ourselves standing in the walled courtyard of a home with a flower garden and a small patch of lush green grass. Blooming vines grew up the walls in the shade of several olive trees and palm trees. Seven pillars supported the second story of a U-shaped, three-sided structure (I was reminded of the home in Proverbs 9:1), and their graceful arches shaded a walkway. In the center of this lovely scene was a fountain. Imagine—coolness, shade, water, grass, and greenery after the dust and heat of the street. Imagine—silence after the clamor of the crowds, hawkers, and animals. Yes, it was paradise! Everything seemed to call out, "Welcome to a place where everything is cared for and every care met."

This week's verse to remember:

"See then that you walk circumspectly, not as fools but as wise, redeeming the time, because the days are evil."

Ephesians 5:15–16 (NKJV)

Dear woman after God's own heart, you—yes, you!—have this same ministry to your loved ones and to all who cross your threshold. How can I say that? Because, as we'll learn in this new section of lessons, when you develop a heart *for* your home, you become the heart *of* your home!

What does it mean to build your home? Not only is the structure and upkeep of the home dealt with in the concept of home building, but the family itself is included. Although the Hebrew word for "house" and "home" is the same, "home" is the preferred word here. A house is not always a home and this verse does not speak of house construction, masonry, or carpentry, but of home building; the knitting together of family and a day-by-day routine of creating a happy and comfortable place for a family to live.

— Robert L. Alden —

Day One: Women Are to Build Their Homes

Proverbs 14:1; 24:3-4; Titus 2:3-5

Hearing from God

1. When a woman after God's own heart develops a heart *for* her home, she becomes the heart *of* her home. Look again at a passage we have studied before: Titus 2:3-5. What does verse 5 command older women to teach younger women regarding their homes?

   _____

2. This command, to be busy at home, seems unnecessary on the surface. Most women I know are always busy. The need is to be busy doing the right things. Read Proverbs 9:1. What builds a home? Prioritize the following phrases according to their importance (e.g., 1 = most important).

   ____ hard work ____ wisdom ____ being submissive ____ rising before dawn

3. Women have incredible power in the home. Read Proverbs 14:1, and complete the following statements based on this scripture:

   The wise woman _____

   The foolish woman _____

4. This scripture does not mention what a foolish woman does to tear down her home, but the context early in Proverbs 14 is righteous versus deceitful speech. What are some things women do that tear down or destroy their homes?

   _____

   _____

   _____

   _____

5. Proverbs 24:3-4 identifies three things needed to build, establish, and furnish a home. List these below.

   _____

   _____

   _____

   _____

6. The most frequently mentioned home-building tool in Proverbs is *wisdom*. But how can a woman after God's own heart acquire the wisdom needed for the complex and busy twenty-first century? God's Word directs us to the answer. Read the following scriptures, and list the sources of wisdom.

1 Kings 4:29 _____

_____

Psalm 51:6 _____

_____

Psalm 111:10 _____

_____

Proverbs 2:6 _____

_____

Responding to God: "Yes, but how?"

7. A woman needs wisdom every day of her life. Think for a moment about today and the week ahead. What issues and problems are likely to arise today and this week that will require you to have wisdom and understanding?

_____

_____

_____

_____

8. Every woman makes mistakes that she regrets or, because of fatigue or distraction, makes less-than-the-best decisions. What are some situations that could jeopardize your home if they aren't handled with wisdom? What are some of the "foolish woman" traps around you?

_____

_____

_____

_____

9. Write out your prayer to God today. Pay close attention to your homemaking and home-building roles as a woman after God's own heart.

_____

_____

_____

_____

What does it mean to tear down your home? It means to pull down or in pieces, break, destroy, beat down, break down or through, overthrow, pluck down, ruin, throw down (demolition, destruction).

LifeScene *Maggie was the third daughter in a home with five children, four of them girls. Because her father worked long hours and barely supported the family, Maggie never had nice clothes, only hand-me-downs. She never forgot the merciless kidding and sneers from other girls at school. When she was older, Maggie set her sights high. She married a doctor, gave birth to three beautiful daughters, and sacrificed so her girls would have all the best. Nearly every day now Maggie gets embroiled in vicious arguments with her girls about what they will wear to school. They refuse to wear the clothes she picks out for them. Often they stash an extra set of clothes in their school lockers and change out of the clothes they wear from home. The more Maggie pushes, the harder her girls push back. Maggie is determined that none of her children's choices in clothing will reflect poorly on her, their mother.*

What is destroying this home, and what is prescribed as a wise remedy?

_____

_____

_____

_____

The garden of God's little girl—how grand!
It began with a dream, a prayer, and a plan.
Nothing this splendid just happens, we know:
It takes time and care for flowers to grow.

— **Elizabeth George** —

Summary

A woman can build her home with godly wisdom, or she can tear it down through foolish choices and decisions. Every woman needs wisdom to build her home. Fearing the Lord and asking Him for wisdom will help a woman build her home.

Father, I need Your wisdom. Today the prayer of my heart is _____

_____

_____

_____

Day Two: Women Are to Watch over Their Homes

Proverbs 31:27; Proverbs 6:6–11; Luke 10:38–42

Hearing from God

1. We have studied the woman of Proverbs 31 in previous lessons. Let's return and look at verse 27 again. Copy this verse in the space below.

_____

_____

_____

_____

2. Jot down the positive action she takes and the negative behavior she avoids.

Positive action: _____

Negative behavior: _____

3. Other passages in Proverbs offer remedies for idleness. Read the verses below, and identify the remedies in the space that follows.

Proverbs 6:6–11 _____

_____

Proverbs 14:23 _____

_____

Proverbs 17:24 _____

_____

Proverbs 28:19 _____

_____

4. If one of these verses inspires you, copy it and post it somewhere so you will see it every day. Memorize it and include it in your prayers as a reminder to build your home.

Responding to God: "Yes, but how?"

5. Read the meaning of the Hebrew words for "watch over" printed in the first column below. Meditate on these words, and apply them to your family. In the next column, jot down an aspect of your home life that you need to watch over. In the right-hand column, identify an action you can take to guard or protect that part of your home and family.

What does it mean to watch over your home? Literally, "to hedge about (as with thorns), i.e., guard, to protect, attend to, keep, mark, look narrowly, observe, preserve, regard, save, make sure, wait, and watch."

	Watch Over What?	How Can I?
To guard, protect	_____	_____
	_____	_____
	_____	_____
	_____	_____
To watch, to look narrowly	_____	_____
	_____	_____
	_____	_____
	_____	_____
To preserve, to save	_____	_____
	_____	_____
	_____	_____
	_____	_____
To make sure	_____	_____
	_____	_____
	_____	_____
	_____	_____

Week Six

6. The enemy of vigilance is idleness, but what is idleness? What is the difference between idleness and rest, which everyone needs to function effectively? How would you define the two?

   To be idle means _____

   _____

   To rest means _____

   _____

7. Perhaps you have heard the adage "Idle hands are the devil's workshop." One biblical illustration of the danger of idleness is found in the life of David, a man after God's own heart. Read 2 Samuel 11, and name the temptation that came through idleness.

   _____

8. Busyness and workaholism are not suitable antidotes to idleness. Martha was busy and concerned about many things (Luke 10:38–42), but Mary made a better choice. How can you watch over your home without becoming a workaholic and a worrisome nag?

   _____

   _____

   _____

   _____

LifeScene   *Reneé wants her family to be secure and happy and to know they are loved. As a child, Reneé didn't have many of the things other children had. Now that she is a successful real-estate agent and her husband, Kevin, is a successful stockbroker, Reneé's family can have the things that appear to provide security and joy in life. Reneé's three children have their own bedrooms, their own computers linked to the Internet, their own cable TVs, and the clothing they have picked out for school. Having her children well supplied frees up time for Reneé to handle real-estate matters in the evenings. Life is busy for Reneé and her family. She is never idle.*

Is Reneé doing a good job of watching over her home? Why or why not?

_____

_____

_____

_____

Summary

God calls women to watch over and guard their homes. Idleness or inattention to the needs of the family often leads to a dangerous breakdown of love, security, and happiness in the home.

Heavenly Father, help me see my home as You see it. Today I pray

_____

_____

_____

Day Three: Women Are to Manage Their Homes

Ephesians 2:10; 5:15-16; 1 Timothy 5:11-15

Hearing from God

1. You and I have little control over most of the events of our lives. But we do have a measure of control over the atmosphere and order of our homes. What goes on under our roofs happens in **our** place—a place we build, watch over, and manage. Let's review the first two ways that you can build a heart for your home.

    Women are to _____

    Women are to _____

2. Paul gave Timothy instructions for leading the church in Ephesus. Read 1 Timothy 5:11-15. How should younger widows spend their time?

    _____

    _____

    _____

    _____

3. Some young widows went in a different direction. What were they doing?

    _____

    _____

    _____

    _____

The greatest blessing...is to have a wife to whom you may entrust your affairs.

— **Martin Luther** —

4. Take your dictionary and read the definition of "manage." Finish the following statement.

    Managing my home means that I am to_____

    _____

5. Diligence is a vital trait for managing your home. Read the following scriptures, and write down the life truths or insights that encourage you to be more diligent.

    Psalm 39:4-5 _____

    _____

    Ecclesiastes 12:13-14 _____

    _____

    Ephesians 2:10 _____

    _____

    Ephesians 5:15-16 _____

    _____

6. Review the four life truths you wrote down in question 5. As you consider these truths, evaluate how careful you are in managing your life and your home in these difficult, evil days. Circle the appropriate description below.

Distracted

Sometimes aware

Vigilant

Responding to God: "Yes, but how?"

7. The way to begin improving your role as manager of your home is to conduct a prayerful walk-through of your home. Grab a notepad and pen. Check off each step as you complete it.

❑ **Examine your heart. Open your eyes.** Ask the Lord to open your eyes to things you may not have noticed before. Ask Him to speak to your heart about the needs of your family and how you can address them.

❑ **Walk through your home.** Walk through each room in your home. If something needs to be picked up or cleaned, take a moment to do so. Pray for each person who occupies or uses that room. Take that person's needs to the Father.

❑ **Make a list.** Create a list of improvements, repairs, or other work needed in each room of your home. After compiling your list, gather the resources you need. Then start to work! This is what a good manager does.

8. Do some ruthless what-if thinking. For instance, to be a better manager of your home, what could be gained if...

you unplugged the TV on certain days? _____

_____

you turned off or disconnected all phones at certain hours? _____

_____

you canceled some subscriptions? _____

_____

LifeScene *Nancy is fifty-five and has been an active Christian for many years. She is married to a busy husband, who travels a lot. She looks after aging parents, who are in declining health. Nancy also has three children—a son in high school, a daughter engaged to be married, and a daughter who is married with children and going through a divorce. Nancy believes she will have to put her mother into an assisted-living facility soon. Her son's grades are hitting bottom. Nancy and her younger daughter are busy planning a wedding. And her older daughter is fighting depression and despair. Nancy has always prided herself on being an able manager, mother, and spouse, but life is coming unhinged. Something changed, however, and life for Nancy greatly improved.*

What do you think changed?

_____

_____

_____

_____

Summary

Women can build their homes by managing themselves and their families well. Tuning out distractions and tuning in to biblical truth about the purpose and goal of life can help women manage their homes to the glory of God and the joy of their families.

Today, Lord, help me be a better manager by _____

_____

_____

_____

Day Four: Women Are to Keep Their Homes

Proverbs 17:1; 21:20; Titus 2:4–5

Hearing from God

1. Titus 2:4–5 should be a familiar passage to you by now. Here it is from the New International Version: *Then they can train the younger women to love their husbands and children, to be self-controlled and pure, to be busy at home, to be kind, and to be subject to their husbands, so that no one will malign the Word of God.* The phrase "to be busy at home" is translated differently in the following Bibles:

   > King James: "keepers at home"
   > New King James: "homemakers"
   > New American Standard: "workers at home"
   > New Living Translation: "take care of their homes"

2. Circle the words that best describe your feelings about keeping your home or being a homemaker.

   drudgery   tiring   unrelenting   joy   satisfying   fulfilling   costly   dull

   sacrifice   proud   improvement   draining   exhausting   rewarding   fun

   impossible   overwhelming   organized   share   chores   helpful   maid

   hopeless   meaningful   procrastinate   stubborn   careful   unfair   done

3. The noble woman of Proverbs 31 was busy at home but also served away from her home. Reread verses 10–31, and list some of the things she did at home and away from home.

   Busy at Home   **Busy Away from Home**

   _____   _____

   _____   _____

   _____   _____

   _____   _____

This little piggy stayed home.

4. Homemaking—keeping your home in good order—blesses your family in many ways. Read these scriptures, and list some of the blessings that come from paying close attention to needs at home.

    Proverbs 17:1 _____

    _____

    Proverbs 21:20 _____

    _____

    Ecclesiastes 10:18 _____

    _____

5. A woman who rarely stays at home to keep her home can be unfaithful on several levels. Read about such a woman in Proverbs 7:10–12, and list ways such a woman fails in her commitments.

    _____

    _____

    _____

    _____

Responding to God: "Yes, but how?"

6. Look at your personal calendar for the previous week and respond to the following questions:

    How many meetings did you have? _____

    How many outings or get-togethers did you have? _____

    How many lunches-out did you have? _____

    How many appointments did you have? _____

    How many evenings-out did you have? _____

    How many days did you shop or run errands? _____

7. Sometimes the drudgery and demands of housework tempt us to find any excuse to get out of the house. Those of us who work outside the home in a full-time or part-time job have to cram housework into a more limited schedule. On the average, not counting time you sleep, how many hours are you home in a typical day?

    _____

    _____

    _____

    _____

8. In a busy, demanding world, every woman needs to have and maintain a schedule. Having a schedule and doing your best to stick to it will help you achieve God's purposes, keep your home in good order, and provide you adequate time for the important things in life. Read Ecclesiastes 3:1–9, and then write out on a notepad a practical, livable schedule for each day of the week.

LifeScene

Barbara is a single mother and has little time to take care of the house. Her children are in grade school and often complain because they can't find their clothes, supper is usually late, and other kids have more things than they do. Barbara feels guilty every day that she has to work and isn't home to clean the house, fix better meals, and buy nicer things for her children. Barbara has learned that the best way to get a promotion at work is to wear more revealing clothes and to be willing to stay late or to work weekends to help her boss. At first, gaining a promotion was not worth the price she would have to pay, but now Barbara is not so sure. Every choice brings its own load of guilt.

Does Barbara have any guilt-free options? What are they?

_____

_____

_____

_____

Summary

A woman builds a heart for her home by keeping her home a place of rest, joy, and provision. By keeping a schedule that helps us be home more often and by devoting ourselves to essentials, we can be successful keepers of our homes.

Today and always, Father, You are Lord of my schedule. Help me to

_____

_____

_____

Day Five: Yes, but How?

Daniel 1; Ephesians 5:16

Hearing from God

1. At times we have the skills to do something but lack the motivation. I am praying that you are motivated and stirred by what you have studied thus far. Let's review the four lessons we have studied this week.

   Women are to   _____

   Women are to   _____

   Women are to   _____

   Women are to   _____

2. Paying attention to what we eat and maintaining a close walk with the Lord are crucial in carrying out the many roles we play in the home. Take a moment to read the challenges that Daniel faced in Daniel 1. How did diet and time with God help Daniel to be God's leader in a difficult era?

_____

_____

_____

_____

I have only just a minute,
Only sixty seconds in it...
Just a tiny little minute,
But eternity is in it.

—Author Unknown—

Responding to God: "Yes, but how?"

3. Here are twelve tips for better time management and several scriptures that we have studied. Read each scripture, and then draw a line from the scripture reference to the time-management tip you believe most resembles that scriptural truth. After connecting the tips and scripture references, number the tips in priority sequence based on your current needs.

___ Plan in detail.		Galatians 5:16–18
___ Deal with today.		Ecclesiastes 9:10
___ Value each minute.		James 4:14
___ Keep moving.		Proverbs 31:15
___ Develop a routine.		Psalm 39:4
___ Watch your diet.		Proverbs 21:5
___ Time flies. Be wise.		1 Corinthians 14:40
___ Keep track of your time.		Proverbs 6:6–9
___ Do the toughest job first.		Ephesians 5:16
___ Study time-management helps.		Daniel 1:8
___ Know when to say no.		Proverbs 14:23
___ Get organized.		Matthew 6:34

4. Review these twelve time-management tips again, and think about how you can apply them to your life. List one goal or action you will take this month related to each tip.

✦ Plan in detail. _____

✦ Deal with today. _____

✦ Value each minute. _____

✦ Keep moving. _____

✦ Develop a routine. _____

✦ Watch your diet. _____

✦ Time flies. Be wise. _____

✦ Keep track of your time. _____

✦ Do the toughest job first. _____

✦ Study time-management helps. _____

✦ Know when to say no. _____

✦ Get organized. _____

5. Think for a moment about the four ways a woman develops a heart for her home: She builds her home. She watches over her home. She manages her home. She keeps her home. Which of these four lessons spoke the loudest to your heart, and what changes are you planning to make as a result?

_____

_____

_____

_____

LifeScene *Stacey became a Christian after her divorce. She remarried and now has three children, one from her first marriage and two from her new husband's first marriage. Raising children in a blended family has been more difficult than Stacey first thought. Joint-custody agreements with ex-spouses threaten to disrupt any routine and peace in their family. Added to the burden are eight grandparents who want to be a part of the picture. Stacey feels totally out of control of her time. She long ago accepted responsibility for mistakes in her first marriage, but Stacey wonders how long she can build her new home without losing her mind.*

How can Stacey build, watch over, manage, and keep her home as she is faced with these challenges?

_____

_____

_____

_____

Summary

Because of the many enemies arrayed against the home in today's culture, women need to understand their biblical, God-given role in building a healthy home. Once we know our roles, we must develop a plan to meet our family's needs and work that plan faithfully.

Lord, give me Your plan for my home. Today I pray _____

_____

_____

_____

Video Notes

Week Seven

A Heart for Spiritual Growth

"The power of maturing in every area of life"

A Heart for Spiritual Growth

"The power of maturing in every area of life"

Proverbs 24:3-4; Ephesians 5:15-16; Titus 2:4-5

Key Truths:

✤ A woman grows in true wisdom in direct proportion to her knowledge of God and His ways.

✤ How we care for our bodies determines whether we are physically available for God's service anywhere at any time.

✤ A woman's spiritual growth is reflected in the nature and depth of her relationships with others.

One of my favorite proverbs is only two lines long, but it clearly sets the direction for an exciting and meaningful life. It's Proverbs 15:14, and in the New King James Version it reads, "The heart of him who has understanding seeks knowledge, but the mouth of fools feeds on foolishness."

To get straight to the point, this verse says that the wise person grows wiser, while the fool grows more foolish. In other words, those who desire to grow, will—and those who don't, won't! Pretty simple, isn't it?

But here's the motivator, the catalyst, the reason and the purpose to grow: our spiritual growth results in spiritual ministry. When you are growing, you can't help but share the overflow of your vibrant life! It's just too exciting and life changing to keep it to yourself!

So where does such growth begin? It starts with your *self.* And what do I mean by "self"? I mean your personal spiritual growth—feeding your mind and soul with the truths from the Bible so that the goodness and strength and insights from God's Word fill and feed your life. When your life is full, your blessings and gifts will overflow into the lives of others. As a result, you minister to others. Your spiritual growth is the mainspring to ministry. The axioms are true: nothing coming in equals nothing going out. You cannot impart what you do not possess. So let the growth begin!

This week's verse to remember:

"And Jesus increased in wisdom and stature, and in favor with God and men."

Luke 2:52 (NKJV)

Day One: The Foundation of Spiritual Growth

Matthew 7:21-27; John 14:23-24; 1 John 2:9-11

Hearing from God

1. The foundation of a woman's spiritual growth is her relationship with Jesus Christ. How firm a foundation is your relationship with Jesus? As you meditate on this question, read Jesus' words found in Matthew 7:21-27, and then answer the questions below.

   Will everyone who says that Jesus is her/his Lord go to heaven? ❑ yes ☒ no

   Will everyone who prophesies, drives out demons, and performs miracles in Jesus' name go to heaven? ❑ yes ☒ no

   Who will be allowed to enter heaven? *Those who do the will of the father*

   What word did Jesus use to describe those persons who claimed to be acting on God's behalf but never did the will of God? *~~bad doers~~ evildoers*

2. Some women and men believe they are going to heaven because they go to church and try to live good lives. Their lives are characterized by verses 26-27. How is your spiritual foundation different from the house built on sand? Read the two statements below, and then complete the statement that best reflects your spiritual foundation.

   A. I hope I will go to heaven, but right now I am not sure, because _____

   _____

   B. I know I will go to heaven when I die, because _____

   _____

3. If you completed the A statement in question 2, call your Bible teacher or another woman in your Bible study group. Share your response with her, and ask her to explain how you can know without a doubt that you will go to heaven when you die.

4. A woman's relationship with Jesus Christ is not based on her desires or behavior. On the other hand, a woman's relationship with Jesus changes her desires and transforms her behavior. Read the following scriptures, and jot down indicators that a person has made a life-changing commitment to follow Jesus Christ.

   John 14:23-24 *Obey my teaching*

   _____

   John 15:5-8 _____

   _____

   Ephesians 2:10 _____

   _____

   1 John 1:5-10 _____

   _____

   1 John 2:3-11 _____

   _____

Responding to God: "Yes, but how?"

5. The fact that you are participating in this Bible study indicates that you have a hunger to know God more deeply. Your hunger is a wonderful sign that your pursuit of the Lord will be rewarded. Read Jeremiah 29:13 and James 4:7–10, and describe God's promises for those who seek Him.

If you seek me you will find me. If you need wisdom, ask.

> *But God, who is rich in mercy, because of His great love with which He loved us, even when we were dead in trespasses, made us alive together with Christ (by grace you have been saved).*
>
> **Ephesians 2:4-5** (NKJV)

6. The foundation of spiritual growth in your life is your relationship with Jesus Christ. The key or the secret to spiritual growth is found in a scripture passage that you have already read. Read it again, and jot down the secret to spiritual growth.

John 14:23-24 *Obey my teaching*

7. Obedience is the key to spiritual growth. Obeying God's Word opens opportunities to grow in your faith. Knowing God's Word is not enough to guarantee spiritual growth. If you continue in this study of *A Woman After God's Own Heart* but do not put into practice or obey what you learn, you will be short-changing yourself. Pause for a moment to evaluate your obedience to God's Word. Circle the number that best reflects your progress in spiritual growth.

5 I am applying the truth of God's Word to every area of my life to the best of my ability, and I try to obey Him in everything.

4 I am applying the truth of God's Word to some areas of my life, and I obey Him most of the time.

3 I occasionally think about God's Word and how it relates to me, but I don't always try to obey Him.

2 I have trouble finding time to read God's Word and seldom think about how to obey God.

1 I just try to live the best I can. I'm not sure what God expects of me.

LifeScene Carmen owns five Bibles, most of which are marked throughout with highlighting pens and notes in the margins. She has studied several Bible reference books and faithfully attends women's Bible studies. Carmen has studied the Bible so much that she is getting bored with some of the studies her church currently offers. She also has occasional disputes with other Bible teachers over how to teach God's Word and believes her pastor's preaching is spiritually shallow. Sometimes she gets frustrated with others and "loses it" by saying something she later regrets.

Is Carmen's spiritual growth on track or off track? Explain.

She is not being patient & kind.

Summary

The foundation of a woman's spiritual growth is her relationship with Jesus Christ. That relationship will be reflected in her behavior and in her other relationships. If a woman has committed her life to Jesus and seeks to obey His Word daily, she can grow spiritually and minister effectively for Christ.

Father, today I surrender myself to You and commit to obey Your Word in every area of my life. Today I pray _To be_ _pleasing to you_

> ### How to Become a Christian
>
> **A**dmit that you are a sinner and that you cannot save yourself.
>
> **B**elieve that Jesus Christ is God's Son and that He died for your sins.
>
> **C**onfess your sins, ask for God's forgiveness, and commit your life to Christ. Follow His example and grow in understanding God's Word.

Day Two: Mental Growth

Luke 2:52; 1 Corinthians 1:18–31

Hearing from God

1. Jesus' growth and maturity inspire us as His followers to grow and mature as well. Read Luke 2:52, and copy the verse below.

   Jesus grew in Wisdom and Stature and in favor with God and men

2. Jesus grew in at least four ways. What are the four ways mentioned in this scripture?

   1. _Wisdom_
   3. _Stature_
   2. _in favor with God_
   4. _"   "   " man_

3. God's Word addresses the way to wisdom and the path to foolishness. Read the following scriptures, and jot down truths about wisdom and foolishness.

   Proverbs 15:14 _The mouth of a fool feeds on folly_

   Proverbs 18:15 _The heart of the discerning acquires Knowledge. The ears of the wise seeks it out_

101

4. Mental growth comes when we actively seek knowledge and wisdom, not when we passively take in vacant, random images and messages. We must seek to grow wise in the ways of the Lord, or we will absorb a mountain of useless folly and frivolity from our culture. Several biblical personalities focused on growing mentally. Read these passages, and write down the names of the persons who sought wisdom and understanding.

Nehemiah 8:1–8 _Ezra_

Daniel 1:17 _Daniel_

Ecclesiastes 1:12–13 _Son of David_

Luke 1:1–4 _Luke_

Acts 18:24–28 _Apollos_

5. In his letter to the church at Corinth, Paul contrasts the wisdom of the world with the wisdom of God. Read 1 Corinthians 1:18–31. How did God, through the sacrifice of His Son, Jesus, make foolish the wisdom of the world?

To so-called wise men and scholars, the gospel is foolishness. Why? _because it is not in the Lord_

What do truly wise people boast about (see v. 31)? _Let those who boast boast in the lord_

Responding to God: "Yes, but how?"

6. Review the past twenty-four hours in your mind. When did you spend time passively absorbing what the world calls wisdom but we know as foolishness? Now look ahead to the next twenty-four hours. What changes can you make in your day that will give you more time for purposefully seeking God's wisdom? Jot down some ideas.

Study rather than TV.

Look over this list and attempt to make these changes during the day ahead.

The wise grow wiser, the foolish more dense.
William MacDonald

7. Now, what do you most want to learn? What spiritual issues or biblical topics interest you? Take some time to pray and think. Then jot down your thoughts. These five topics will become your Five Fat Files (see marginal note).

A. _____

B. _____

C. _____

D. _____

E. _____

Write each of these topics on an expandable file folder. As you study the topics, file your notes in the appropriate folder.

Your expandable file folders will become your treasured "fat" files as you fill them with magazine articles, newspaper clippings, sermon notes, class outlines, and Bible study notes. Set up your Five Fat Files today!

LifeScene

Greta is a busy wife, mother, and pharmaceutical rep for a national drug company. She packs more into her busy day than most women can accomplish in two days. She gets her family up each morning and off to school and work. She visits several doctors' offices every day and reads volumes of literature on drug interactions and sales techniques. Her few hours at home are spent cleaning, cooking, being with her family, and finally collapsing in bed.

How can a busy woman like Greta find time in her day to grow in godly wisdom through His Word?

_____
_____
_____
_____

Summary

As followers of Jesus Christ, we can grow in wisdom only as we actively and purposefully seek to know God and His ways. A woman after God's own heart will actively structure her day to include time in God's Word.

Today, Lord, the prayer of my heart is ___Make me more aware of my need for Christ___

Day Three: Physical Growth

Matthew 26:39–46; 1 Corinthians 6:12–17; 9:24–27

Hearing from God

1. What does physical growth have to do with spiritual growth? By looking at many Christians today, you would think that following Jesus adds extra weight to the stomach, hips, and thighs. At a time of intense agony in Jesus's life, the physical condition of his disciples weakened their spiritual power. Read Matthew 26:39–46. How does our physical condition limit our spiritual power?

   _____

   _____

   _____

   _____

2. The apostle Paul disciplined himself and trained his body to meet any and every opportunity for sharing the gospel. Read 1 Corinthians 9:24–27. Why did Paul want to make his body his slave?

   _____

   _____

   _____

   _____

3. What race is Paul describing? What is this competition in which every believer is engaged?

   _____

   _____

   _____

   _____

4. What prize are we running to win? _____

   _____

5. As women after God's own heart, we need to understand the relationship between our bodies and the Holy Spirit. Read 1 Corinthians 3:16 and 6:12–17. Describe this relationship in the space that follows.

   _____

   _____

   _____

   _____

6. The way we care for our bodies, the food we eat, and the exercise we get directly influence our spiritual health and our witness for Jesus Christ. Read 1 Corinthians 10:31. What should influence the way we eat and how we treat our bodies?

   _____

   _____

   _____

   _____

7. If you need any further encouragement to pay attention to your food choices and the care of your body, read Romans 13:13–14. Summarize in your own words the challenge stated in these verses.

_____

_____

_____

_____

Responding to God: "Yes, but how?"

8. As you have contemplated the relationship between your physical condition and your spiritual condition, how have you seen your physical condition limit your spiritual life or your witness?

_____

_____

_____

_____

9. As you think about factors that influence your physical condition, resist the temptation to make commitments you know you cannot keep. Instead, identify just two practical, doable steps you can take to improve your physical condition in the following areas.

Sleep   (1) _____

           (2) _____

Food   (1) _____

           (2) _____

Beverages (1) _____

           (2) _____

Exercise   (1) _____

_____(2)

And the angel of the LORD came back the second time, and touched him, and said, "Arise and eat, because the journey is too great for you." So he arose, and ate and drank.

1 Kings 19:7-8a (NKJV)

LifeScene Connie is married with two preschool children. Before she had children, Connie was a fitness freak. She used to run three miles every day, count fat grams, and wear a size 2. During the past four years, her body has borne the brunt of motherhood. A world she used to control and enjoy is now reduced to a TV, hundreds of toys, spills, and her only refreshing oasis—the refrigerator. Connie's extra weight makes her self-conscious about going out in public, especially to church. She has not attended her small-group Bible study for several months.

You are Connie's friend and an active member of her small group. How do you reach out to her?

_____

_____

_____

_____

Summary

A woman after God's own heart needs to care for her body in such a way that she is physically available for God's service at any time. As the temple of the Holy Spirit, our bodies can limit our witness and spiritual power if we fail to discipline ourselves and overcome life's many temptations.

Father, I need Your help and power for improving my physical health. Today the prayer of my heart is _____

_____

_____

_____

_____

Day Four: Spiritual Growth

Romans 8:29; Ephesians 6:10–11; Philippians 1:9–10

Hearing from God

1. God has a plan for our spiritual growth. He wants us to mature for a purpose. Read Romans 8:29 and 2 Corinthians 3:18, and write down the reason we need to mature as women after God's own heart.

    _____

    _____

    _____

    _____

2. Spiritual growth should lead us to acquire skills, characteristics, and attitudes that change us and influence others. Read the following scriptures, and note the abilities and strengths we gain as we grow spiritually.

    Ephesians 6:10–11 _____

    _____

    Philippians 1:9–10 _____

    _____

    Colossians 1:10–12 _____

    _____

    James 1:22 _____

    _____

3. Studying God's Word is helpful for spiritual growth. Read the following scriptures, and identify how knowing God's Word can make a difference in your life.

    Psalm 119:11 _____

    _____

    Psalm 119:28 _____

    _____

    Psalm 119:45 _____

    _____

    Hebrews 4:12 _____

    _____

    1 Peter 1:23 _____

    _____

> *Oh, how I love Your law! It is my meditation all the day.*
>
> —**Psalm 119:97** (NKJV)—

4. Studying God's Word is not enough for meaningful spiritual growth. Read James 1:22–25, and jot down what must be added to Bible study to achieve spiritual growth.

    _____

    _____

5. Spending daily time with God in prayer also brings spiritual growth and power. Read the following scriptures, and identify the blessings and power that can be gained through faithful prayer.

    James 1:5 _____

    _____

    Acts 10:30–33 _____

    _____

    Philippians 4:6–7 _____

    _____

    James 5:15–17 _____

    _____

Responding to God: "Yes, but how?"

6. If you have grown spiritually since becoming a follower of Christ, what benefits and blessings have you experienced as a result of your spiritual growth?

    _____

    _____

    _____

    _____

7. How has spiritual growth influenced your relationships in your family?

    _____

    _____

    _____

    _____

8. The fruit of spiritual growth is often referred to as the fruit of the Spirit. Galatians 5:22–23 focuses on this fruit. Read this passage, and list the attributes you need in greater abundance.

_____

_____

_____

_____

9. If you want to experience in greater abundance the attributes you have listed in question 8, you need to continue growing spiritually. How can you be more intentional in your growth?

_____

_____

_____

_____

LifeScene

Roberta has been a Christian for many, many years. Throughout her life she has exhibited a quick temper. She has prayed and asked God to help her control her temper. She has read books about anger management and self-control. But Roberta still struggles. Roberta's husband, Quincy, is not a believer and refuses to go to church. He tells Roberta that he doesn't need religion. Quincy often points to Roberta's temper as proof that religion doesn't change people. Quincy calls Roberta a hypocrite because she goes to church every Sunday and still can't control her temper. Whenever Quincy says this, Roberta loses it and lets him have it.

Will things ever change with Quincy and Roberta? Why or why not? What will help?

_____

_____

_____

_____

Summary

Spiritual growth is essential for greater peace, direction, purpose, and victory in life. By studying and obeying God's Word and spending daily, meaningful time in prayer, a woman can grow spiritually and be more effective in ministering and witnessing in her world.

Today, Lord, the prayer of my heart is _____

_____

_____

_____

Day Five: Social Growth

John 13:34–35; Ephesians 4:32; 5:21; 1 Thessalonians 5:12–15

Hearing from God

1. So far we have studied the mental, physical, and spiritual aspects of personal growth and development. Now we will focus on the fourth area mentioned in Jesus' life. How does Luke 2:52 describe this area of growth?

    And Jesus grew in wisdom and stature, and in favor with God and _____.

2. What does it mean for you to be in favor with others? _____
    _____

3. Just as we grow mentally, physically, and spiritually, we must mature in how we treat others, especially other believers within our church. Read the following scriptures, and summarize how we should think of and treat brothers and sisters in Christ.

    John 13:34–35 _____
    _____

    Ephesians 4:32 _____
    _____

    Ephesians 5:21 _____
    _____

    Colossians 3:13–14 _____
    _____

    1 Thessalonians 4:18; 5:12–15 _____
    _____

    James 5:16 _____
    _____

    1 Peter 3:8–9 _____
    _____

    1 Peter 4:7–10 _____
    _____

4. Look back at your responses to question 3. Think about your relationships within your church. In the left margin next to each scripture reference, grade yourself on your faithfulness in that area (e.g., A = Excellent; C = Fair; F = Poor).

5. If we are not maturing in our relationships within the church, how can we grow in favor with those outside the church? Read the following scriptures, and then note why you think people responded so positively to Jesus.

Matthew 7:29 _____

_____

Mark 6:34 _____

_____

Luke 19:1–7 _____

_____

John 8:3–11 _____

_____

At every encounter, make it your aim that people are better off for having been in your presence. Attempt in every encounter to give something away, to give something to the other person.

Responding to God: "Yes, but how?"

6. Evaluate your social growth within the church by rating yourself in the following areas. (1 = Never; 2 = Seldom; 3 = Often; 4 = Consistently)

_NO_   I seek to increase my circle of friends every week.

_4_   I work quickly to forgive, and I am not bearing a grudge against anyone.

yes   I spend more time listening to others than I do talking.

_____   I do not say negative or critical things about others even if I believe those things are true.

yes   I encourage my pastor(s) verbally and speak well of him to others.

_____   I serve others by helping and doing acts of kindness without expecting thanks.

_2_   I am on the lookout for newcomers in our church and go out of my way to befriend them.

_____   If someone offends me, I go to that person in private and discuss the matter with him or her and seek to be reconciled.

_____   People who know me say that I am a positive person who always believes the best about others.

_____   I am using my spiritual gifts by serving others in my church.

7. On a separate sheet of paper write a prayer asking the Lord to put into your heart a greater desire to grow in every area where you scored less than 3. Place the prayer sheet where you will read it every day.

LifeScene

Darlene has been a church member for almost five years now. During that time she has noticed that many women in her age group have their own small circle of friends and show little interest in her. Any attempts they make toward befriending her come across as patronizing and insincere. When Darlene's second child was born, only one woman—Kathy—made a real attempt to reach out to Darlene and celebrate the special event. To Darlene, church seems more of a social congress in which groups of close friends try to impress one another and protect their group from outsiders. She has decided to play the game and not rock the boat, but she cares very little about most of the women in her church.

If you were Darlene, would you do the same or something different? Explain.

_____

_____

_____

_____

Summary

As we grow spiritually, we also grow socially in our relationships inside and outside the church. God's Word gives us many challenging instructions and examples of how we should treat, love, and serve others. If our relationships within the church are not growing, our relationships outside the church are probably poor as well.

Father, give me a heart that submits to others and desires to serve them. Today I pray _____

_____

_____

_____

```
        V i d e o   N o t e s





```

Week Eight

A Heart for Service

"Spiritual growth equips us to serve God."

A Heart for Service

"Spiritual growth equips us to serve God."

Psalm 37:4-5; Isaiah 40:28-31; 1 Corinthians 12

Key Truths:

❖ A woman's spiritual growth overflows in service to her family, church, and others who need Christ.

❖ Setting goals for spiritual growth increases the likelihood that we will succeed.

❖ God equips us for service by giving us spiritual gifts to use within the church to build up the Body of Christ.

Maybe it's because I used to teach English, but I pay careful attention to verbs, the part of each sentence that indicates action. And I can't help but notice that verbs like *strive, reach, press, endure, fight, run,* and *continue* are liberally sprinkled throughout the New Testament. I want you to think about these verbs now and the effort they imply. Why? Because, dear heart, we are pressing toward the goal of finishing our Bible study, of understanding what it means to be a woman after God's own heart, a woman who possesses a heart for service.

This week of lessons takes us through the reaching and straining phases of running our race! We are moving fast! And we are going to cover a lot of ground in this leg of the run. But take heart. The goal line is in sight.

Spiritual growth is worth every effort, every self-disciplined action, every purposeful step of desire and dream. Not only are we blessed by each step we take but others around us and in our future will be blessed and enriched by the overflow. Our spiritual growth can be enhanced and quickened if we will make God-centered choices and set goals. Goals help focus our attention and reduce confusion and wasted motion.

Every woman whom God uses spends time—sometimes years—in preparation. Even trials and crises can be God's classroom to teach us faithfulness and persistence. The

This week's verse to remember:

"Delight yourself also in the LORD, And He shall give you the desires of your heart. Commit your way to the LORD, Trust also in Him."

Psalm 37:4-5a (NKJV)

Bible lists the stories of many women whose lives changed history and influenced a nation. But there are even greater stories being written right now—as you study, read God's Word, and dare to follow Him. Every woman who steps out in faith to serve and meet the needs of others is making an indelible mark in eternity.

Day One: Spiritual Growth Is Worth Striving For!

Hebrews 11:7–40; Exodus 3:7–14

Hearing from God

1. Spiritual growth always leads to more effective ministry, and it blesses others as our lives spill over in service to our family, our church, and others who need Christ. Through encounters with God and faith in His Word, many biblical characters served God's purposes in their day. Read Hebrews 11:7–40, and describe the service provided by each person below as he or she grew in faith.

   Noah _____

   Abraham _____

   Joseph _____

   Moses _____

   Rahab _____

2. Often people are reluctant to serve. Do you remember when I told you about my reluctance to teach a women's Bible study? Perhaps you are one of those reluctant ones. Read the following scriptures, and list the names of persons who were reluctant to serve and, if indicated in scripture, why they hesitated.

   Exodus 3:7–14 _____

   _____

   Judges 6:11–24 _____

   _____

   Esther 4 _____

   _____

   1 Samuel 10:17–27 _____

   _____

   Jonah 1:1–3 _____

   _____

   Acts 9:10–16 _____

   _____

3. With the exception of Saul, all of the persons listed in question 2 were effective in serving God even though they were reluctant at first. Check each of the following statements that explains why these biblical leaders were effective in service.

   ❏ They were educated, trained people and were born leaders.
   ❏ They were good communicators and could express themselves well.
   ❏ They were godly people and great students of God's Word.
   ❏ Everybody admired them and looked up to them.
   ❏ They obeyed God and did whatever He told them to do.

Responding to God: "Yes, but how?"

4. Spiritual growth is worth striving for. Already you have been encouraged to start your Five Fat Files. List the five subjects that you plan to study as you pursue spiritual growth.

   1. _____
   2. _____
   3. _____
   4. _____
   5. _____

5. The ideal way for a woman to pursue spiritual growth is with the aid of a mentor (see Titus 2:3-5). If you know some older women who could mentor you, write their names below.

   Possible Mentors: _____

   _____

6. Another way to pursue spiritual growth is through classes or Bible studies provided by your church. Call your church or several evangelical churches in your area, and list some of the classes available to you.

   _____
   _____
   _____

It was said of John Wesley, the brilliant founder of Methodism and one who was heralded as a shining example of consecrated intellect, that he was a "man of one book—The Book!"

— J. Oswald Sanders —

7. Seeking wise counsel from a Bible teacher, your pastor, or a godly woman is a great way to begin charting your path for spiritual growth. Write down the names of people who fit these descriptions.

   _____
   _____
   _____
   _____

8. What will you do this week to implement one or more of the suggestions in questions 5, 6, and 7?

   _____
   _____
   _____
   _____

Week Eight

LifeScene — *Holly was asked by her pastor to lead a women's Bible study at her church. Holly loves to study the Bible and enjoys participating in her Sunday School, but she is terrified of teaching a group. She thanked the pastor for the invitation but declined, saying that she is not yet ready to lead a group. Her pastor asked when she thought she would be ready. Holly didn't have an answer for that question but blurted out, "I don't know. Maybe later."*

When do you think Holly will be ready to lead a Bible study? What signs will indicate that she is ready to serve?

_____

_____

_____

_____

Summary

Spiritual growth blesses others as our lives spill over in service to our family, our church, and others who need Christ. Although we may be reluctant to step forward and serve, the Lord will bless our efforts whenever we trust Him and obey His leadership in our lives.

Today, Lord, give me the heart of a servant. I pray _____

_____

_____

_____

Day Two: Spiritual Growth Is Aided by Goals and Choices

Psalm 37:4-5; Proverbs 10:24; 16:3, 9

Hearing from God

1. All of life is interconnected. Your decisions at home, at work, and in your heart influence everything else in your life. Every decision you make can aid or prohibit your spiritual growth. Read the following scriptures, and note whether the decision helped or hurt the persons involved.

   Genesis 3:1-6 _____

   _____

   Genesis 13:8-13 _____

   _____

2 Samuel 11:1–4 _____

_____

1 Kings 3:3–15 _____

_____

Matthew 19:16–22 _____

_____

2. Setting worthy goals helps us focus on what is most important in life. Sometimes we shy away from setting goals because we fear failure or because we want to keep our options open in case more attractive choices appear later. Read the following scriptures, and jot down the blessings or values of setting God-centered goals.

Psalm 37:4–5 _____

_____

Proverbs 10:24 _____

_____

Proverbs 16:3, 9 _____

_____

Proverbs 21:5 _____

_____

3. In going to the city of Corinth to share the gospel, Paul set a self-limiting goal. Read 1 Corinthians 2:1–5. Write down Paul's goal for his ministry in Corinth and why he chose that goal.

_____

_____

_____

_____

4. What other goals did Paul set for his remarkable life?

Romans 15:20 _____

_____

Romans 15:28 _____

_____

2 Corinthians 5:7 _____

_____

Philippians 3:14 _____

_____

5. Read again Proverbs 16:9. What does this scripture say about the importance of seeking God's leadership in setting goals?

_____

_____

_____

_____

You cannot be with people all the time and have a ministry to people.

You cannot kill time without injuring eternity.

Aim at nothing, and you will hit it every time.

Week Eight

117

Responding to God: "Yes, but how?"

6. If you want to be a wise woman, read this acrostic and think about how these actions can lead to godly wisdom. Consider how to adopt these ideas in your life.

   Willingly give your life to Jesus Christ. *(Have I?)*
   I dentify sin in your life. *(Do I?)*
   S hed spiritual laziness. *(How can I?)*
   D ecide the method and rate of growth. *(How am I doing?)*
   O bligate yourself to be mentored. *(Have I asked someone?)*
   M aintain spiritual growth. *(Am I actively seeking or coasting?)*

7. What other goals have you set for yourself in various aspects of your life?

   _____

   _____

   _____

   _____

8. Based on what you have studied and considered today, what goals do you want to set for establishing time to grow spiritually and to gain a heart for service?

   _____

   _____

   _____

   _____

LifeScene — *Juanita wants to do the right thing, and she wants people to think well of her. As a result, Juanita cannot say no. She is room mother for her son Carl's third-grade class. She is president of her home-owners association. She attends three Bible studies during the week, one that meets across town. She tries to exercise at least three times a week, and she volunteers in preschool Sunday School at church. Most of the time Juanita is exhausted, frustrated, and burdened with guilt over being unable to do every-thing that she has committed to do. She knows she needs to simplify her life, but she is afraid to drop out of anything that will hurt what people think about her. She decides to keep juggling her hectic schedule and live with her load of guilt rather than disappoint others.*

Did Juanita make the right decision? What else could she have done?

_____

_____

_____

_____

Summary

We can achieve greater strides in spiritual growth and service if we will make God-centered choices and set goals in important areas. Goals focus our attention and our energies on what is most important, and they reduce confusion and wasted motion in our lives.

Today, Lord, the prayer of my heart is _____

_____

_____

_____

Day Three: Spiritual Growth Requires Time

Isaiah 40:28-31; Matthew 11:11

Hearing from God

1. Spiritual growth begins in our relationship with Jesus Christ and is aided by purposeful focus, discipleship, and goals. Spiritual growth depends on the choices we make. Spiritual growth also requires time in God's Word—*a long time*. Read the following scriptures, and write down the blessings that came to each person after being faithful for many years.

    Genesis 5:32-6:22 _____

    _____

    Genesis 21:1-7 _____

    _____

    Genesis 41:39-46 _____

    _____

    Luke 2:25-38 _____

    _____

2. God is able to sustain us over the long haul. Read Isaiah 40:28-31, and answer the following questions.

    Does God get tired and worn-out? _____

    What does God do for people who are weary and weak? _____

    _____

    What does God do for those who place their hope in Him? _____

    _____

    How does God transform the abilities of those who wait upon Him? _____

    _____

3. Every person used by God spends time in preparation. They may not realize they are being prepared. They may be living in obscurity, serving quietly behind the scenes without fanfare or acclaim. They may have no idea how their current trials are equipping them for God's service. How did each of these biblical personalities spend their lives before they became major spiritual leaders?

    Joseph (Genesis 39-41) _____

    _____

    Moses (Exodus 3:1) _____

    _____

    David (1 Samuel 16:1-12)_____

    _____

    Elisha (1 Kings 19:16-21) _____

    _____

    Saul/Paul (Acts 8:1-3) _____

    _____

But has in due time manifested His word through preaching, which was committed to me according to the commandment of God our Savior.

Titus 1:3 (NKJV)

4. John the Baptist spent most of his life in obscurity. His time as a prophet, preparing the way of the Lord, was brief. Read Matthew 11:11. Explain in your own words what Jesus said about John the Baptist.

_____

_____

_____

_____

Responding to God: "Yes, but how?"

5. As you have studied how several biblical leaders spent time in preparation, what insights have you gained into your own preparation and service?

_____

_____

_____

_____

6. List five truths about the Lord, His Word, His purposes, yourself, or the church that you have gained during your months or years of preparation and spiritual growth.

   1. _He loves me_____
   2. _He forgives me_____
   3. _Hes is faithful_____
   4. _____
   5. _____

7. Do you think that the time spent in preparing to serve God is intended to prove your ability to God or to prove God's ability to you? Or are other things accomplished during lengthy preparation?

_____

_____

_____

_____

LifeScene Hope's brief life inspired everyone she touched. She was born with critical heart and spinal problems. Her first years were spent in and out of the hospital as she underwent several surgeries. As a child Hope committed her life to Christ and was baptized by her pastor and father. Even though she was confined to a wheelchair, she always encouraged others and loved the Lord. As a teen, she committed her life to the gospel ministry. After college she went to seminary and prepared to serve the Lord as a youth leader. Two weeks before graduation, Hope's heart just stopped beating, and she died in her sleep. The entire seminary faculty, her friends, and others who had been touched by her life were stunned. How could God allow her life to end just as she was finishing years of preparation?

As Hope's friend, you are asked to speak at her funeral. What do you say about Hope's life?

_____

_____

_____

_____

Summary

Every person used by God spends time in preparation. We may not realize we are being prepared, but God works in many ways to prepare us to serve and bless others. Our role is to be faithful in everything and obey Him all along the way.

Father, help me accept every day as a gift from You. Today, as I prepare to serve You, I pray _____

_____

_____

_____

Day Four: Spiritual Growth Results in Spiritual Ministry

Acts 9:36-41; 16:11-15; 18:1-19

Hearing from God

1. The Bible presents shining examples of women who fulfilled God's design for service. These women were filled with the grace and power of God. That grace and power overflowed as ministry to others. Let's study the example of their lives.

   A. **Dorcas**—Acts 9:36-41

   What was her service record? (v. 36) _____

   _____

   What was a tangible record of her ministry in her church? (v. 39) _____

   _____

   What could be written about your service record? _____

   _____

   B. **Lydia**—Acts 16:11-15, 40

   Where do we first meet this woman, and why was she there? _____

   _____

   How did God work in her heart and through whom? _____

   _____

   What was her first act of obedience as a follower of Jesus Christ? _____

   _____

   What was her first act of service? _____

   _____

   How did her home become part of her ministry? _____

   _____

And many women who followed Jesus from Galilee, ministering to Him, were there looking on from afar, among whom were Mary Magdalene, Mary the mother of James and Joses, and the mother of Zebedee's sons.

Matthew 27:55-56
(NKJV)

C. **Priscilla**—Acts 18:1–3, 18–19; 1 Corinthians 16:19; 2 Timothy 4:19

How was Priscilla's ministry different from that of Dorcas and Lydia? _____

_____

What did Priscilla do that you can do in your church? _____

_____

D. **Phoebe**—Romans 16:1–2

How did Paul describe her and her service in his letter to the church in

Rome? _____

_____

What does this woman's service tell you about her faithfulness in

ministry? _____

_____

Some Bible scholars believe she may have carried Paul's letter to Rome.
If so, Paul had great trust in her faithfulness.

How does a woman build a reputation for faithfulness? _____

_____

Responding to God: "Yes, but how?"

2. As you studied the lives of these four women, what messages did you receive
from God's Word?

_____

_____

_____

_____

3. How can today's study help you grow spiritually and minister better to others?

_____

_____

_____

_____

4. Write a brief note about yourself that you hope could be included in your obit-
uary. In the note summarize what you would like people to remember about
your life and ministry to others. Complete this sentence with your own words.

She was most beloved for the way she _____

_____

_____

_____

_____

LifeScene

Ingrid was not a beautiful woman, nor was she well known in her church. You knew her if you were a parent because Ingrid worked with bed babies in the youngest preschool class. Most people saw her as a babysitter, a matronly woman who rocked babies, changed their diapers, and sang them songs about Jesus and the Bible. Some mothers were hesitant at first to bring their newborns to church, afraid they might catch a cold or fuss or be inconsolable. But after their babies had spent one or two Sundays with Ingrid, they never worried again. Ingrid's voice could transform a baby from tears to a look of wonder. In winter, in summer, when worship services went long, on rainy days, and all other days, Ingrid was there with her smile and comfortable shoulder.

What did Ingrid's ministry mean to her church, and what did her ministry cost her?

_____

_____

_____

_____

Summary

Throughout the Bible and in hundreds of thousands of churches, women have given their lives to serve and meet the needs of others. Some of these women's names will be remembered for centuries, but all will be remembered for eternity.

Father, I want to be a woman You can use to minister to the heart of Your church. Today I pray _____

_____

_____

_____

_____

Day Five: Spiritual Ministry Is Aided by Spiritual Gifts

Matthew 20:28; 1 Corinthians 12

Hearing from God

1. Christianity is a relationship with Jesus Christ that results in service to others. Read Matthew 20:28, and write down what Jesus said about why He came into the world.

   _____

   _____

   _____

   _____

2. God prepares us for service by giving us spiritual abilities or spiritual gifts. What did Paul write in 1 Corinthians 12:1 about our understanding of spiritual gifts?

_____

_____

_____

_____

3. Read verses 4–6. How is there diversity yet unity in the expression of spiritual gifts in the church?

_____

_____

_____

_____

Do all the good you can,
By all the means you can,
In all the ways you can,
In all the places you can,
At all the times you can,
To all the people you can,
As long as ever you can.

—John Wesley —

4. Read verse 7. Which persons in the church receive spiritual gifts, and how are these gifts to be used?

_____

_____

_____

_____

5. Read verse 11. Who determines who receives a certain gift? _____

6. Read Ephesians 4:11–16. God gives various gifts to people in the church to prepare God's people for what?_____

7. According to verses 12–16, what happens within the church when people use their spiritual gifts as God directs?

_____

_____

_____

_____

8. Read these other scriptures on spiritual gifts, and write down truths that you learn: Romans 12:6–8; 1 Peter 4:11.

_____

_____

_____

_____

Responding to God: "Yes, but how?"

9. Every believer has at least one spiritual gift for use in building up the church. If you know your spiritual gift(s), describe it and explain how you are using it in your church.

_____

_____

_____

_____

10. If you do not know your spiritual gift(s), ask your Bible teacher or pastor to guide you in discovering your giftedness. Responding to the following questions will start you on the road to discovering your gifts.

A. What service do you do within your church that brings you the most joy?

_____

B. What do you do within your church that people say blesses them the most?

_____

C. What do you do within your church that energizes rather than exhausts you?

_____

D. What do you do within your church that best reveals Christ's love in you?

_____

LifeScene

Tanna always told other members of her Bible study group that she did not have any spiritual gifts. She loved Bible study, but she did not want to teach because she was intimidated by talking in front of a group, even a small group. She did not want to be in charge of anything because she said she was totally unorganized. So Tanna told everyone not to ask her to do anything. However, whenever a woman in the class was ill, Tanna fixed a meal and took it to the woman's family. If a woman went into the hospital, Tanna took care of the family's children and cleaned their house. Whenever the Bible study group met, Tanna always provided coffee, juice, and something she had cooked. Whenever Tanna helped another woman or her family, she was happier and more alive than at any other time.

Is Tanna correct in saying she has no spiritual gifts? How would you reply to her?

_____

_____

_____

_____

Summary

God prepares us for service by giving us spiritual abilities or spiritual gifts. Every believer has at least one spiritual gift that is to be used within the church to serve others and build up the body of Christ. When we use our spiritual gifts as God directs, we are energized, and God's church is strengthened.

Lord, give me insight into my spiritual gifts, and empower me to serve You. Today I pray _____

_____

_____

_____

Video Notes

dicipleship
Taking Classes - Bible study
Council - Interview
Go to Church looking
Read
spirtual growth is aided
by growth.
Choices - priorities
you cannot kill time without
injuring eternity'
success it the meeting
of preperation and opturnity

Week Nine

A Woman After God's Own Heart

"Becoming the woman God created you to be"

Week Nine

A Woman After God's Own Heart

"Becoming the woman God created you to be"

Proverbs 11:24; Matthew 6:21-23; Philippians 2:5-8

Key Truths:

❖ Growing in Christlikeness transforms our priorities and opens every facet of our lives to the power of God.

❖ A woman after God's own heart seeks to do good for the family of God.

❖ Because life is fleeting, we must make the most of every day.

I will never forget visiting "The Seven Sacred Pools" hidden away on the island of Maui, Hawaii. Here's the scene. Water overflows from the top pool, high and covered in a perpetual mist, and falls into another...and another...and another. The overflowing continues until all seven pools are filled, and the water eventually pours into the vast Pacific Ocean.

Dear one, *that's* what this entire study has been about! First, we place ourselves before God for His filling of our hearts and souls. When our hearts are brimming, they overflow into the lives of our husband and children. As we live out God's love in these priority areas, the overflow spills into our home. Then, as we think and pray about others, the preparations for service begin. Eventually our lives overflow in ministry to countless others, as far-reaching as the ocean.

Understanding and living by God-centered priorities set us free to resist the downward pull of selfishness and greed. When we are most aware of God's grace and goodness to us, we can become God's very hands and feet of mercy to people in need.

God's Word helps us understand that doing good begins with the people of God and His church. By doing simple, inexpensive things like writing notes, making phone calls, and memorizing scriptures, a woman can lift a weary heart and encourage a church's spiritual leaders. When we learn the secret to spiritual giving, we unleash a joy that few people know or have ever experienced. I'm asking you to think more and pray more as we bring our study to a close. In this final section, "A Woman After God's Own Heart," it's all about you...and your heart!

Day One: Mastering Yourself and Your Priorities

Matthew 6:21–23; 15:16–20; Mark 7:17–23

Hearing from God

1. A person's priorities are seen in the way she or he lives. Everyone has a set of priorities, but few people can easily identify or admit what those priorities are. Read the following scriptures, and write down what you believe were the priorities of these Bible characters.

   Noah (Genesis 6) _____

   _____

   Joseph (Genesis 39–41) _____

   _____

   Moses (Exodus 14) _____

   _____

   Achan (Joshua 7) _____

   _____

   Joshua (Joshua 24:15) _____

   _____

   A young man (Matthew 19:16–22) _____

   _____

   Barnabas (Acts 9:26–30) _____

   _____

   Demetrius and Alexander (Acts 19:23–41; 2 Timothy 4:14–15) _____

   _____

2. Reread the story of the noble woman in Proverbs 31:10–31. Write down what you believe her priorities were.

   _____

   _____

   _____

   _____

3. Jesus taught people to think about where their desires and actions began. Read the following scriptures, and note what Jesus said about our priorities: Matthew 6:21-23; 15:16-20; Mark 7:17-23.

_____

_____

_____

_____

4. Step outside of yourself for a moment, and be as objective as possible. Watch yourself go through a typical day. Based on what you see yourself doing, what would others think your priorities are?

_____

_____

_____

_____

5. What do the following scriptures say is the key to mastering the downward pull of selfishness, greed, and self-centered living?

Psalm 119:11 _____

_____

Ecclesiastes 12:13-14 _____

_____

Romans 8:5-14 _____

_____

Galatians 5:13-26 _____

_____

Two roads diverged in a wood, and I—
I took the one less traveled by,
And that has made all the difference.

— Robert Frost —

Responding to God: "Yes, but how?"

6. Now that you have been engaged in this study for more than eight weeks, how have your priorities changed?

_____

_____

_____

_____

7. During this study, we have focused on a woman's relationship with God and her role in her marriage, family, home, and personal life. You have also chosen topics for developing your understanding in five spiritual areas (Five Fat Files). How do you think the topics you have chosen will enrich your life in each of the following areas?

A woman after God's own heart _____

_____

A wife _____

_____

A mother _____

_____

A leader in the home _____

_____

A ministry leader _____

_____

LifeScene

Marta is always the epitome of organization, determination, and discipline. She and her husband, J. T., have raised four sons even though the family has never had much money or many of the finer things in life. When asked about her admirable work ethic, Marta usually talks about her midwestern parents and their strict German ways. She also talks about how studying God's Word is an important part of her life and her family's life. Some people in their church think Marta and J. T. are too strict and need to loosen up, but others admire the way they have loved and provided for their family. When Marta was asked to give her testimony at a women's retreat, she spoke about three people in the Bible who influenced her life.

Who might those three people have been, and why?

_____

_____

_____

_____

Summary

Our priorities are seen in the way we live. Focusing on God's Word and growing in Christlikeness will transform our priorities and give us victory over selfishness and worldly values.

Father, please expose the things in my life that displease You.

Today I pray _____

_____

_____

Day Two: Learn to Reach Out and Look Out

Proverbs 11:24; 1 Timothy 6:17–19

Hearing from God

1. We often do not realize the lasting impact of a cheerful smile, a kind word, or a pat on the back. God reveals his loving-kindness to us in many ways, and His Word urges us to reach out and do the same for others. Describe the loving acts reflected in the following scriptures.

   Genesis 2:15–18 _____

   _____

   Genesis 21:14–21 _____

   _____

   Exodus 16:11–18 _____

   _____

   Ruth 2:1–16 _____

   _____

   1 Samuel 2:18–21 _____

   _____

   Luke 15:4–7, 11–32 _____

   _____

   John 3:16 _____

   _____

   John 13:1–17 _____

   _____

2. Read Luke 6:27–38, and focus on Jesus' radical teachings on love, grace, and giving. Write down a truth that you gain from each scripture listed below.

   vv. 27–29 _____

   v. 30 _____

   v. 31 _____

   v. 35 _____

   v. 36 _____

   v. 38 _____

3. Take a moment to read Proverbs 11:24. Have you ever experienced the truth of Proverbs 11:24? If so, describe your experience in the space below.

   _____

   _____

   _____

   _____

> *Beloved, let us love one another, for love is of God; and everyone who loves is born of God and knows God. He who does not love does not know God, for God is love.*
>
> **1 John 4:7-8** (NKJV)

4. The apostle Paul instructed Timothy how to teach wealthy believers to live. Read 1 Timothy 6:17–19, and summarize Paul's message in the space below.

_____

_____

_____

_____

Responding to God: "Yes, but how?"

5. Most of us fail to look out for and reach out to others, not because we are indifferent, but because we are too busy. We pass by the wounded person on the roadside, not because we are heartless, but because we have too many appointments on our calendars. Read the story of the good Samaritan in Luke 10:30–37, and fill in the two columns below.

What did the Samaritan do to help the injured man?	_What did this act of kindness cost the Samaritan–financially and otherwise?_
_____	_____
_____	_____
_____	_____
_____	_____
_____	_____

6. Write down two things you can do today to look out, reach out, and give.

1. _____

2. _____

LifeScene

Sharon suffers from an illness that requires daily medication and careful attention. For years she was afraid to travel, fearful of becoming ill in a foreign country. When her church launched a mission project to help people in the war-ravaged country of Afghanistan, Sharon and her husband read about the plight of the Afghan people, the influence of Islam, and the need for Christians to minister in that war-torn country. After great prayer and sleepless nights, Sharon and her husband volunteered to go to Kabul to help with the project. While in Afghanistan, Sharon sensed the Lord's power as never before, and she remained healthy throughout the trip. She returned home with an open heart and a deep concern for Muslims and a desire to share Christ with them.

How are you like Sharon? How are you different?

_____

_____

_____

_____

Summary

We often do not realize the lasting impact of a cheerful smile, a kind word, or a pat on the back. God reveals His loving-kindness to us in many ways, and His Word urges us to reach out and do the same for others.

Today, Lord, give me eyes to look out and a heart to reach out and give. I pray _____

_____

_____

_____

Day Three: Do Good to All but Especially to the Household of Faith

Galatians 6:10; Hebrews 4:12

Hearing from God

1. Paul encouraged believers in Galatia to "do good to all people, especially to those who belong to the family of believers" (Gal. 6:10). Today we will focus on three ways you can minister to and do good to those in your church. One way to do good is to write notes. Read Isaiah 50:4. How did God equip Isaiah to help others?

    _____
    _____
    _____
    _____

2. Read Luke 1:3. In what way did Luke hope his writing would benefit Theophilus?

    _____
    _____

3. What benefit do you think the world has received from Luke's writing the Gospel of Luke and the book of Acts?

    _____
    _____
    _____
    _____

4. How can a ministry of writing notes to your pastors and church members help fulfill 1 Thessalonians 5:11?

    _____
    _____
    _____
    _____

By the way, handwritten notes sent through the mail or delivered to the door are more meaningful and enduring than quick e-mail messages.

5. Making phone calls is another way to do good. Too often women and men misuse the telephone. Read 1 Timothy 3:11 and Titus 2:3. How can the phone be misused?

_____

_____

6. How can the telephone be a ministry tool and a great method for encouraging other believers?

_____

_____

_____

_____

7. A third way to do good to other believers is to memorize scripture. When someone is hurting and you don't know what to say, scriptures that you have memorized may come to mind so you can share them at just the right moment. What do the following scriptures say about the power and usefulness of scripture?

2 Timothy 3:16–17 _____

_____

Hebrews 4:12 _____

_____

Life is mostly froth and bubble,
Two things stand like stone,
Kindness in another's trouble,
Courage in your own.
Adam Lindsay Gordon

Responding to God: "Yes, but how?"

8. Writing notes, making telephone calls, and memorizing scriptures are not only meaningful ministries, but they are ministries you can do "on the run." Whenever you come upon some unexpected free time in your busy day, you can stop, write a note, make a call, or memorize a scripture. Here are some tips for making the most of free moments.

Writing Notes — *Carry a pen, a small box of note cards, prestamped envelopes, and a printed church directory in your car.*

Making Calls — *Keep a church directory in your car, and use your cell phone to call and encourage others.*

Memorizing Scripture — *Print scriptures on index cards, and keep them in your purse or car.*

9. Take a moment to write the names of your pastors and church members who need encouragement right now. List the reason for contacting each person. Use one of the three ministries you studied today to encourage these believers.

Church Member   **Reason to Contact**

_____   _____

_____   _____

_____   _____

_____   _____

_____   _____

LifeScene *Mildred loved her church and wanted to serve the Lord throughout her life. At the age of seventy-eight, she had to limit her trips out of her home, so she asked her pastor what she could do to minister from home. He asked her to write letters to new church members and welcome them to the church family. So Mildred did. Not only did she write letters to new members, she also wrote letters of encouragement to her pastors and others in the church. Not only did she write letters, but she also prayed for each person as she addressed the envelopes. Several years later Mildred died. The church could not hold all of the people who attended her funeral.*

Think about Mildred's life. How are you and Mildred alike? How are you different? What have you learned from her?

_____

_____

_____

_____

Summary

Every woman who follows Christ is to "do good to all people, especially to those who belong to the family of believers." We can do good by writing notes, making telephone calls, and memorizing scriptures. What good will you do for your church this week?

Today, Lord, the prayer of my heart is _____

_____

_____

_____

_____

Day Four: Spiritual Giving

Matthew 9:36; 10:5-8; Philippians 2:5-8

Hearing from God

1. A woman after God's own heart can make a big difference in the lives of others through a Christlike attitude and a giving spirit. Today we will look at four ministries you can have anywhere, any day, at any time. The first ministry is **giving totally wherever you are**. Read Matthew 10:5-8, and fill in the missing word from verse 8.

   "Freely you have received, freely _____*."*

2. Read Matthew 14:16. In a remote area, far from food, Jesus commanded His disciples to do something unusual. Fill in the missing word.

   Jesus replied, "They do not need to go away. You _____ them something to eat."

3. Give totally wherever you are. Before you leave home, plan to give, pray to give, and go to give. Make the objective of every trip outside your home to give, and you will be surprised at what the Lord can do through you. What is the next trip you plan to take, and what could you give?

   _____

   _____

   _____

   _____

4. **Serving** is another powerful ministry that every woman can and should have. Read again the ultimate example of service in Philippians 2:5-8. Through His life, how did Jesus serve others?

   _____

   _____

   _____

   _____

5. Think about your life. In what ways are you serving others, especially through your church?

   _____

   _____

   _____

   _____

Wherever you are, be all there. Live to the hilt every situation you believe to be the will of God.

—Elisabeth Elliot —

6. **Showing mercy** is another rare but powerful ministry that relates to caring for and helping others. Such ministry overflows from an attitude of the heart. Read Matthew 9:36; 14:14; and 20:34. Then write down the key word that describes this attitude of the heart.

   _____

7. Pause and look around you. Who is hurting, ill, or lonely? Who needs God's mercy extended through you today?

   _____

   _____

   _____

   _____

8. The fourth powerful ministry is **giving financially**. Such giving is to be done with simplicity, with no thought of return or gain for yourself. What do the following scriptures teach about giving?

   Proverbs 31:20 _____

   _____

   Mark 12:41-44 _____

   _____

   Acts 4:36 _____

   _____

9. Giving our money to help others is one of the toughest ministries in the twenty-first century. Why do you think so many believers struggle in the area of giving?

_____

_____

_____

_____

10. Who in your church body needs a portion of the funds that God has entrusted to your stewardship?

_____

Responding to God: "Yes, but how?"

11. Review the four ministries we have studied today. In the spaces below, jot down one doable idea for each of these ministries. After listing something in each area, pray and then give. Start today!

Give totally wherever you are. _____

Serve. _____

Show mercy. _____

Give financially. _____

LifeScene Rheba's husband died suddenly just a year before retirement. Rheba was devastated and didn't know how she could go on. But Rheba had always loved mission work and giving to others. After selling her home and moving into a smaller house, Rheba continued to lead a women's mission group at her church. Now she and other women collect clothes and food for needy families. Every month they volunteer at a free health clinic to label and organize donated pharmaceuticals. Rheba serves on her church's missions committee and participates in local and international mission trips. Though living on a limited income, Rheba gives generously to help others. She also loves to sing in the adult choir and senior adult choir.

What qualities does Rheba have that you admire and want to see in your own life?

_____

_____

_____

_____

Summary

Yes, a woman after God's own heart can make a big difference in the lives of others through a Christlike attitude and a giving spirit. You can develop a heart for ministry by giving totally wherever you are, serving and helping others, showing mercy to the sick or lonely, and giving financially.

Father, I earnestly desire a heart for ministry. Today I pray _____

_____

_____

_____

Day Five: The Woman You Want to Become

Ecclesiastes 6:12; James 4:14; 1 Peter 1:24

Hearing from God

1. The Bible says that life is fleeting. Read these scriptures, and jot down words or phrases that biblical writers used to describe the brevity of life.

   Ecclesiastes 6:12 _____

   _____

   James 4:14 _____

   _____

   1 Peter 1:24 _____

   _____

2. Because life passes so quickly and then is over, we must be careful with every day the Lord gives us. If we are not careful, we will waste not only time but a precious life. Take a moment to review these nine weeks of study and prayer. Look back through every lesson. In the spaces below, jot down two truths you learned each week.

   All my possessions for a moment of time.

   —Queen Elizabeth I—

   Week 1: A Heart for Blessing in Prayer _____

   _____

   Week 2: A Heart for Passion in Prayer _____

   _____

   Week 3: A Heart for Discipline _____

   _____

   Week 4: A Heart for Your Husband _____

   _____

   Week 5: A Heart for Your Children _____

   _____

   Week 6: A Heart for Your Home _____

   _____

   Week 7: A Heart for Spiritual Growth _____

   _____

   Week 8: A Heart for Service _____

   _____

   Week 9: A Woman After God's Own Heart _____

   _____

Responding to God: "Yes, but how?"

3. Think about the spiritual woman you want to be one year from today. Pause for a moment until you have a clear mental image of your becoming that person. Now describe the woman you want to be by filling in the paragraph that follows.

One year from today the date will be *0-5-06*, 2*06*.
I will be *69* years old. A year from now the following events will have taken place in my family: _____

_____

_____

_____

I will have made great progress in becoming a woman after God's own heart. By this date, I will be a woman who _____

_____

_____

_____

As I grow spiritually in one year to become this woman, I will—by God's grace—

_____

_____

_____

4. On a separate sheet of paper, expand your vision to ten years from now. Repeat the process in question 3, but change "one year" to "ten years" and complete the same open-ended statements.

5. Once you have completed these paragraphs, you have a road map for spiritual growth. What will you do today to advance your dreams of becoming a woman after God's own heart?

_____

_____

_____

6. You have already gained so much from studying God's Word, spending time with the Lord in prayer, and talking and praying with other women. At the end of this lesson is a prayer I have written to help you live out God's plan for your life. I hope you will make it your prayer as you follow after Christ...all the days of your life.

LifeScene *A woman very much like you just finished a nine-week study on becoming a woman after God's own heart. Although she was a busy person with numerous responsibilities, she was inspired by the study and really wanted to grow spiritually. At times she felt overwhelmed as she considered the many areas of life in which she needed to grow spiritually, but she knew she was not alone. The Lord was with her. A year later the ones closest to her could see a real difference in her life. She was truly becoming a woman after God's own heart, and she had a joy that touched every area of her life.*

What do you think this woman did during those twelve months that had such a positive impact on her spiritual growth?

_____

_____

_____

_____

Summary

Life is fleeting, and we must make the most of every day. To become the women God wants us to be, we must be careful how we live and how we use our time. By setting personal goals, spending time in God's Word, and being available every day to give of ourselves and share with others, we can become women after God's own heart.

Today, Lord, help me take an important step toward becoming a woman after Your heart. I pray _____

_____

_____

_____

A Prayer for Living Out God's Plan

1. **Pray over your priorities.** "Lord, what is Your will for me at this time in my life?"

2. **Plan through your priorities.** "Lord, what must I do today to accomplish Your will?"

3. **Prepare a schedule based on your priorities**. "Lord, when should I do the things that represent these priorities today?"

4. **Proceed to implement your priorities.** "Lord, thank You for giving me Your direction for my day."

5. **Purpose to check your progress.** "Lord, I have limited time left in my day. What important tasks do I need to focus on for the remainder of the day?"

6. **Prepare for tomorrow.** "Lord, how can I better live out Your plan for my life tomorrow?"

7. **Praise God at the end of the day.** "Lord, thank You for a meaningful day, for a day well-spent, for I have offered my life and this day to You as a 'living sacrifice.'"

Video Notes

2 Timothy 1-9
1. Master your priorities   by Math
                             by Model

2. develope yourself - Luck 10-27
3. Learn to reach out - give to all men
   Become the liberally soul
   determin to withold nothing
4. Luke 15-4 look for someone
   who needs help.
5. Write note
   makeing phone calls.
   Give totally wherever you are.
   a. Serving & help others
   b. Mercy.
   c. Giving

Bestselling Titles from the Heart of
Elizabeth George

Elizabeth's bestselling book, from which this series was adapted, has helped tens of thousands of women discover the genuine peace and joy that comes when they pursue God's priorities in every area of their lives—family, home, work, ministry—and become women after His heart.

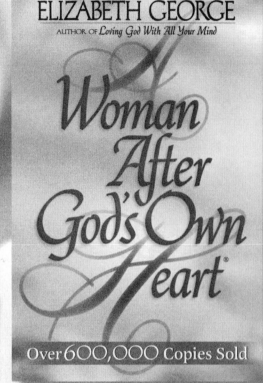

ELIZABETH GEORGE
AUTHOR OF *Loving God With All Your Mind*

A Woman After God's Own Heart

Over 600,000 Copies Sold

Deluxe Hardcover   Growth & Study Guide

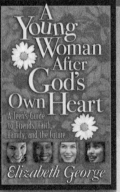

Discover God's plan and purpose for your friendships, faith, family relationships, and future.

Elizabeth reveals what the Bible really says about how to have a good—no, an exceptional!—marriage

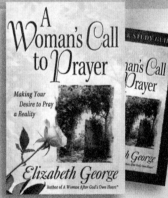

You can have an exciting prayer life! Discover the inspiration and motivation you need to make your desire to pray a reality.

Discover God's guidelines for managing the seven major areas of life more efficiently and effectively.

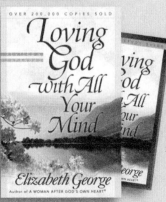

Focus your mind on six powerful Bible truths that will transform the way you think, feel and live.

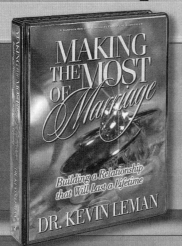
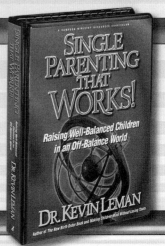
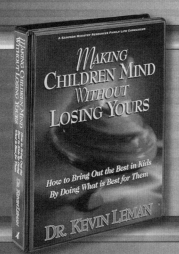
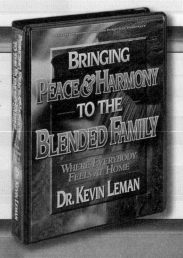